PROPAGANDA

VS

FACT

•

ROSS J. McLENNAN

PROPAGANDA VS. FACT

Copyright © 1978 by
Ross J. McLennan

All rights reserved.

PREFACE

I make no apology for what some may consider "nitpicking" the liquor industry and the product they ardently push. The propaganda used by the promoters of alcoholic drinking has been based on half-truths, innuendos, superstition and out-right lies. Nevertheless, their propaganda, as all propaganda, has succeeded because it has been repeated over-and-over-again and passed on from generation to generation with seldom a questioning voice raised in opposition.

In this little volume — purposedly made brief — I have sought to expose the liquor industry for what it is — a gigantic, colossal, and often a conglomerate corporation whose chief drive for public approval revolves around its lust for profits even if society in general is destroyed. The individual, the family, the state, the nation and the entire human race is looked upon as a potential consumer of the drug they push. Therefore I maintain they are the biggest drug pushers mankind has ever known.

Twenty-five years ago I spoke on the subject of "Propaganda versus Fact" in a large Presbyterian church in Pittsburgh, Pennsylvania. Following the service a distinguished looking man, but one with "fire in his eyes", came up to me, identified himself as a vice-president of the Overholt Distillery, and with emotion cracking his voice stated that I could come to his home and search the house from attic to basement; "But", he said, "You would not find one drop of beer, wine or liquor therein — we don't drink."

I replied, "If what you state is true, why is it you and the liquor industry keep pushing a product that can wreck anyone, — and yet you won't even allow it in your own home?"

Looking me straight in the eye he said, "That's simple, — liquor is not for drinking, — liquor is for selling."

Since that time in 1953 I have met a score or more of owners of wineries and breweries, vice presidents of liquor corporations, wholesalers and retailers who have told me practically the same story of their personal total abstinence stand on the use of alcoholic drinks — they don't use the products they push, — but their love for easy profits dominates their lives.

As a concerned citizen who has not always been a "dry" I am attempting in this little volume to set before the reader some of the main propaganda items that must be exposed for what they are.

NO ENEMIES

You have no enemies you say?
A craven's boast, my friend;
You are a coward in the fray.
A mighty conflict rages,
With right 'gainst wrong arrayed;
The Call to Arms! ring out,
The battle's on! 'tis not a dress parade.
No enemies? Alas, then be ashamed;
The Christ could not so say,
For He was hissed, maligned, defamed
Amid the conflict of His day.
Awake, oh Coward! Draw thy sword,
The Master calls thee; Up and fight!
Hearest thou not the ringing call? forward!
Up, and charge the lines of wrong with right!

—A Soliloquy by A. P. Gouthey.

WHERE'S GRANDMA?

The story is told of a man who was preparing to take a bath. The water faucet was turned on—wide open—the tub was quickly filling up. Suddenly the telephone rang. The fellow dashed into the adjoining room picked up the telephone receiver and in irritation cries, "Yes?" It was the boss from his office—the man calms down and listens intently while he receives instructions on a very important contract,—but during all this conversation the water pouring into the bath tub reached the top of the tub and spilled over on to the floor and flooded the bathroom and was running into the adjoining room where the fellow sat talking at the telephone.

Suddenly, the intended bather sees the water—drops the telephone—rushes into the bathroom grabs a large bathtowel and starts mopping up the water and ringing out the towel in the wash basin. In desperation he calls for his wife. She rushes in and sees the water running all over the floor. She dashes into the kitchen—grabs a mop and pail and rushes to the bathroom and starts mopping up the water that was still flowing over the side of the tub from the open water faucet.

Because of the noise and panic scene created by the man and his wife as they mop and ring out the towel and mop, the young son awakens and stumbles into the scene—he sees the deplorable mess being created by the overflowing tub and the frantic efforts of his father and mother—he grabs the drinking glass sitting next to the toothbrush holder and starts to bail the water out of the overflowing tub and pours the filled glass into the toilet stool.

Finally, grandma wakes up because of the energetic activity, noise and confusion, she surveys the situation—walks into the bathroom—reaches down and shuts off the faucet.

Ridiculous? Of course, but it is a close analogy to the hundred and one do-gooders, alcoholic rehabilitation programs sponsored by the federal government, state government, county government, churches, community action groups. All well intentioned in dealing with the victim of alcohol. But "where's grandma?"

Multiplied hundreds of millions of dollars are being spent every year in a futile attempt to mop-up the problems created by the liquor industry. The alcoholic population is increasing faster than a hundred thousand rehabilitation programs can effectively mop-up the problem drinkers.

The faucet of booze, liquor advertising, glamorizing of drinking, increases daily, and the viscious, corrupt, money-hungry, drug pushing liquor industry piously goes on its debasing and debauching way peddling a drug and a "disease" that Dr. Robert V. Seliger, of Harvard University and the World Health Organization, says "can claim anyone and from which no one is immune."

Mopping up is necessary but *first* shut off the faucet!

CONTENTS

PROPAGANDA REGARDING ALCOHOL

BEER PROPAGANDA

WINE PROPAGANDA

Propaganda Item

LAWS, RIGHTS, TAXES, AND LIQUOR CONGLOMERATES

Propaganda Item

PREVENTION AND REHABILITATION PROPAGANDA

Propaganda Item

THE PROHIBITION ERA

Propaganda Item

"Drink is commercially our greatest wastrel;
—Socially it is our greatest criminal;
—Morally & religiously it is our greatest enemy."
—Albert Schweitzer

PROPAGANDA REGARDING ALCOHOL

How often have you heard that question asked? Basically the individual who asks "What's wrong with one drink?" doesn't want an answer. The question is asked as a defense mechanism for their own actions.

Is there anything wrong with just one can of beer or one cocktail? Within the past few years several studies have come forth that should shake up the so called "social drinker."

DRINKING AND BREAST CANCER

The National Institute of Health study reveals that alcohol consumption increases risk of breast cancer, skin cancer and thyroid cancer. The study was undertaken following the Third National Cancer Survey which showed positive associations between alcohol and breast, thyroid and skin cancers.

A top research scientist and internal medicine specialist, Dr. Roger R. Williams, who conducted the study for the National Institute of Health, states,

> "Alcohol stimulates the secretion of hormones in the pituitary gland, which speeds up cell reproduction — and this increases susceptibility to the development of a malignancy."

With the tremendous increase in breast cancer in women and the rise in the total number of women who use alcohol, the research by Dr. Williams seems even more relevant. He maintains,

> ". . . according to our figures, drinking increases chances of breast cancer in women 20 to 60 percent, of thyroid cancer in men and

women 30 to 150 percent, and malignant mela-
noma (skin cancer) 20 to 70 percent."

"These odds were consistently indicative of a
positive association with all three forms of
alcohol—beer, wine and hard liquor."

How much alcohol must one consume to be listed
in the "endangered zone" of developing cancer?

Dr. Williams' study, recently published in the prestigious British medical journal, *The Lancet*, was
based on 1,127 cases of breast cancer, 709 cases of
thyroid cancers and 89 cases of melanomas, and the
affected persons drank as little as one drink a month
to as much as one half-pint of liquor a day. The more
a person drank, the greater the chance of cancer.

What's wrong with one drink???

A similar study at the University of California at
Los Angeles School of Public Health confirms Dr.
Williams' findings.

The Journal of the National Cancer Institute (53:
631-639, 1974) contains a study by Drs. N. E. Breslow
and J. E. Enstrom which points out that a high correlation was seen between beer drinking and cancer
of the lower bowel and of the breast in women and
of the kidney and bladder of men. The correlation
between beer consumption and cancer of the rectum
in men was especially high. Cancer of the esophagus
was most strongly related to consumption of spirits.
Other cancer sites positively related to spirits consumption were the nasopharynx and the pancreas in
women, and the small intestine in men.

A check at any large city or state library will produce scores of research projects dealing with the
relation of alcohol to cancer of the throat, the upper
respiratory and digestive passages, especially the
mouth floor, pharynx and esophagus.

It's interesting to know that this alcohol-cancer relationship in humans is documented evidence, but the U. S. Congress, HEW, and the Pure Food and Drug Administration don't seem to know what to do. However, they act with diligence and swiftness when it was discovered that saccharine caused cancer in mice. No evidence has yet come forth that saccharine causes cancer in humans but a government agency nevertheless steps in to protect the citizens. The power of the beer and liquor industry shows up so clearly in Congress and in various state legislatures and bureaucratic agencies.

Only one company in the United States makes saccharine, while the beer, wine and liquor industry has breweries, distilleries and wineries in practically every state.

DRINKING AND HYPOGLYCEMIA IN CHILDREN

A father gives his pre-teen child a bottle of beer to "teach him how to drink and so he won't sneak around and get it somewhere other than at home." Some parents feel a glass of wine with the meals somehow teaches the child "to drink acceptably." Smart parent? Hardly! In fact, foolish parent would be more definitive.

Dr. William Altemeier, director of pediatrics service at General Hospital in Nashville, Tennessee warns that severe irreversible brain damage can result from "just one can of beer" by pre-teen children.

"Alcohol is a special danger to children because it tends to cause hypoglycemia, which is a drop in blood sugar," Dr. Altemeier said. "The brain needs blood sugar to function, so, if the blood sugar drops for long enough, brain damage or retardation can occur."

"Parents may not know how dangerous hypo-glycemia is," Dr. Altemeier said. The child does not have to be drunk to have this condition. Just one occasion of very low blood sugar can cause permanent damage unless the child receives medical attention in an hour or two."

Dr. John Wilson, assistant professor of pediatrics at Vanderbilt University agrees with Dr. Altermeier.

"Children under the age of 10 would be most susceptible to this condition. . . . Just one can of beer could affect the intellegence and motor areas of the brain."

What's wrong with just one drink???

DRINKING AND THE BRAIN

Several studies on alcohol's effect on the brain have been very revealing. Everyone knows that heavy drinking can cause physiological damage, but new startling evidence has come forth which indicates that even one drink kills brain cells—and brain cells are irreplaceable.

Until the recent study by Dr. Melvin H. Knisely and his associates, Drs. Herbert A. Moskow and Raymond Pennington, at the Medical University of South Carolina, almost all researchers believed that an occasional drink did no harm to an individual.

Dr. Knisely, long recognized in the scientific world as an outstanding research scientist, discovered during his research on agglutination (blood sludging) that even one drink kills brain cells Our bodies can create all type cells needed for functioning except brain cells. The drinker cannot make the decision as to which brain cells are destroyed with each drink.

Because of this distinction of brain cells, the chronic alcoholic though he may stop drinking, will seldom return to his chosen profession because the knowledge he has had stored in that "computer brain" no longer is available to him. Once a brain cell is destroyed, it is gone forever.

Dr. Knisley further has pointed out the danger a pregnant woman who drinks brings to the unborn child. Not only will the consumed alcohol kill the brain cells of the mother, but it will penetrate the placenta and bring its destruction to the fetus. He believes a great percentage of mental defects in the new born have been due to the cocktail drinking pregnant mother.

What's wrong with just one drink????

CHILD ABUSE — THE ALCOHOL CONNECTION

The director of the National Council on Alcoholism, Dr. Frank Seixas, speaking at the Third Conference on Alcohol Abuse and Alcoholism said scientists are exploring the "fetal alcohol syndrome" which means a baby suffers brain damage from alcohol — prior to birth.

Continuing he states, "If a woman drinks very heavily during pregnancy, she has a high chance of having a baby born with mental deficiency and other congenital abnormalities."

"And the baby's sleep pattern is all crazy," Seixas said. "If the mother is an alcoholic already and pretty tense and nervous . . . and then she has this kid whining and crying more than the average baby she's more likely to be out of patience with it and you have a battered child in addition to all the other things that are wrong."

No one knows how many children are abused each year, but in 1976 public agencies received over 300,000 reports of suspected child abuse. Each year about 2000 children die in circumstances in which abuse or maltreatment is suspected. It is only recently that researchers have begun to look at the relationship between alcoholism and child abuse and neglect. Studies reveal that parents with alcohol problems have a high potential for exhibiting neglect of their children, especially through erratic and inconsistent parenting.

Dr. Henry Kempe, first to describe the "battered child syndrome," maintains that alcohol plays a part in approximately one-third of child abuse cases. In many more cases, he adds, alcohol can be related in some way to the family problem that led to the child abuse.

In a study of incest victims, Y. M. Thomas reports that alcohol frequently seems to be a factor in father-daughter incest occurrences.

For further inquiry into the child abuse problem see *Alcohol, Health and Research World,* produced by the National Institute of Alcohol Abuse and Alcoholism, Washington, D.C.

THE STEPPING STONE SYNDROME

And then there is the "stepping stone syndrome." This is the pattern that develops as one engages in the drug scene.

Dr. Leroy C. Gould of Yale University made a survey and study of teenage drug users. His report published in the May 1977 issue of the *Archives of General Psychiatry* notes that the order of progression in the drug problem begins with alcohol. Then it moves into marijuana, hashish, barbiturates, amphetamines, LSD, mescaline, cocaine and finally heroin. It is revealing that alcohol is the starting drug for most youth who are on other drugs.

What's wrong with just one drink?
PLENTY!!!

> # PROPAGANDA
> **"Moderate drinking never hurt anyone."**

BIRTH DEFECTS AND ALCOHOL

In the early 1970's a team of medical researchers at the University of Washington School of Medicine at Seattle stumbled into a study which in turn stimulated a great many research projects regarding the effect of an expectant mother's drinking upon the fetus.

The study was published in *The Lancet,* a prestigeous British medical journal.

Dr. Kenneth L. Jones, the Seattle pediatrician who headed the study stated, "We fell into this study almost by accident, but we think we have the first reported association between maternal alcoholism and what I would call malformations in their offspring."

Dr. Jones and his associate, Dr. David W. Smith, came upon four children suffering malformations and each child had a mother who was obviously an alcoholic. Dr. Jones said, "That sent us back to the files, where we'd been compiling facts on children's syndromes, and we found that four more children who answered to the same kinds of problems and had the same kind of mothers."

The doctors admit it is a small study as it involves only eight children and eight mothers. It was also the first known study of its kind so they figured they were breaking new ground in a field where taboos are still very much a part of every day business.

The Seattle pediatricians found a pattern of malformity among all eight children though they came from three different groups. Two were white, three were black, and three were American Indians. Five of the malformed children were girls and three were boys.

Several years ago there was "the thalidomide scare" which was linked to severe birth defects. The governments of the world immediately prohibited the manufacturing and selling of thalidomide. More recently various studies have shown that children born to mothers who are heavy smokers have tended to be underweight and pregnant women were urged to stop smoking. However, when the evidence started to accumulate following the Jones-Smith study which pointed out the physical abnormalities in babies born to drinking mothers, the press and news media have been rather sparse in their editorial comments. Why?

What malformities did the children with alcohol using mothers possess? Three had heart murmurs at birth, all, however, corrected themselves. One was born with a condition that forced her blood to bypass her lungs, a defect that had to be corrected at once with open heart surgery. Two of the children were born with dislocated hips. Three cannot extend their arms all the way. Five suffered the deviations of the retarded. Their hands shake when they try to pick up small objects or toys and they have trouble holding on to pencils and crayons. Also they often bang their heads against the wall when left alone.

Almost all the children have one cheek bone smaller than the other which gives their faces a lopsided look. All have small eye openings and one has eyelids that don't open all the way. Several have ears with a "cauliflower" look.

Dr. Smith said the I.Q. range of the children was from below 50 to 80 with the average of 63.

The research team concluded that because of the similarity of the children's abnormalities and the fact that their parents represented a range of racial and educational backgrounds that the mothers drinking was the link to the abnormalities. The team discounted the possible role of malnutrition, which is common among alcoholics, because the children of malnourished nondrinkers don't show a pattern of defects, and although small at birth, they usually catch up in growth shortly after birth. The investigators place the basis of the trouble on the effect of alcohol upon the fetus.

This study from the University of Washington confirms the research from the Medical School of South Carolina published in 1970 in which the eminent Dr. Melvin Knisely and his staff had successfully proven that even one drink kills brain cells.

When Dr. Knisely was questioned as to whether the one drink which would kill the brain cells of the drinker would also kill the brain cells of a fetus of a pregnant woman who drinks, he was most positive in declaring that such was the case.

When one consumes alcohol, the alcohol does not have to go through the digestive process but it is absorbed through the walls of the stomach and picked up by the blood and carried to all tissues of the body—and this includes the fetus or the unborn child.

Mothers that drink while carrying an unborn child are sowing the seeds of destruction to some part of that child and particularly to the brain of the child.

Brain cells are irreplaceable—once they are destroyed they will not replace themselves as do all other cells of the body.

If alcohol is a dangerous drug, why do people drink?

Alcohol has been declared as "the ignored drug with the polished image." Why is it ignored?

Among the social reasons for ignoring the dangers of alcohol is that many do not even classify it as a drug. The marijuana of the hippies, the heroin of the junkie, the LSD of the hallucinates who leap from buildings: those are the drugs that get attention and worry the establishment.

Many social drinkers, particularly those with a sophisticated self-image, laugh off the effects of alcohol. Yet even one mild drink hampers both intelligence and efficiency and kills brain cells.

A second social reason for ignoring the dangers of the alcohol drug is due to its well-informed and highly shined image. The liquor industry in the United States grosses $12 billion a year, and spends nearly $300 million on advertising, a figure exceeded only by car and food ads.

The liquor ads unfailingly associate the consumption of the drug with sex, success, smartness, elegance, youth, health and beauty. Shrewdly, they often stress the high integrity of the liquor maker; occasionally this is a hooded monk — Brother Timothy is popular — or Benedictine wine made by monks, or wine made by the Christian Brothers. Such advertising seeks to give a religious approval to drinking. Never is any mention made to the fact that alcoholism is a grave problem to Roman Catholic and Episcopal priests and that the Roman

Catholic church has at least two alcoholic rehabilitation centers for priests who have become addicted to alcohol.

A report proposed by the Bishops' Committee on Priestly Life and Ministry and released by the National Conference of Catholic Bishops reveals that approximately 5% of the Roman Catholic clergy in the United States suffers from alcoholism.

The report states, "For the first time we have at hand sufficient statistical reports from dioceses and religious congregations that allow us to say with some confidence that the rate of Catholic clergy alcoholism is approximately 5%."

It is noted in the report that clergy alcoholism is more than a big-city problem for "it is proportionately present in the smallest as well as the largest, dioceses and religious orders."

The report also declares that almost 75% of the clergy who have undergone treatment for alcoholism are maintaining sobriety.

The Guest House at Lake Orion, Michigan, opened in May 1956, another in Rochester, Minnesota, opened its doors in 1969. Over 1,700 priests and brothers have recovered and returned to their religious functions since the inception of the program.

A program for Episcopal clergy is conducted by the Recovered Alcoholic Clergy Association in San Francisco.

Legally, sale of the alcohol drug is more and more widely sanctioned. The Prohibition repeal legislation that began in 1933 culminated when the last remaining statewide ban on liquor sales ended in Mississippi. Beyond this, the drug has been available over the counter without prescription and, despite such laws as forbidding sales to minors and known inebriates. It is virtually available to anyone who is half-determined to get it.

The federal government takes in $9.6 billion a year on liquor taxes, second only to individual and corporate income taxes. Hence, weakly devised and lamely enforced controls are allowed to stand, lest the golden egg-laying goose be killed. State Legislatures are eagle-eyed by the powerful liquor lobbies and seldom pass alcohol control legislation because of industry opposition.

Did you know that 1 out of 10 families know the anguish that comes with having a child with a birth defect?

Did you know every year 250,000 babies are born with significant birth defects?

Did you know at least 16,000 infants die in their first year because of birth defects?

Did you know 500,000 unborn babies die every year as a result of birth defects?

These facts are released by the National Foundation of March of Dimes.

Each year when I receive a letter soliciting money for the March of Dimes, I write them a letter and suggest that they get involved in research about birth defects due to the use of alcohol by either or both the father and mother. If alcohol does bring about chromosomal damage as some research scientists maintain, or if alcohol consumed by a pregnant woman has destructive consequences upon the child, it is time that the National Foundation of March of Dimes jumps into the battle and exposes the liquor industry for what it is — a pusher of America's most abused and destructive drug — one that destroys not only the alcoholic but the unborn child.

Since the "kick off" study by Drs. Jones and Smith several birth defect centers are studying alcohol related birth defects under a contract from the National Institute of Health.

Dr. Jamie Frias, Director of the Birth Defects Center at the University of Florida documented the defects of over 50,000 defective children born to women who drank heavily during pregnancy. Besides the general mental retardation, he lists such defects as crossed eyes and small eye openings, smaller than normal head circumferences, cleft palates, ear abnormalities and several forms of congenital heart disease.

Moderate drinkers have 55% more congenital anomalies than abstainers. Heavy drinkers have 355% more congenital anomalies than abstainers.

Dr. Frias concludes, "Present evidence does not favor the hypothesis that the fetal alcoholic syndrome is caused by malnourishment. . . . The causative agent appears to be the alcohol itself."

If alcohol is the causative agent in the fetal alcoholic syndrome the next question usually raised is — "How much must a pregnant woman drink to be classed as dangerous to the fetus.

"When the fetal alcoholism syndrome was first described four years ago, it was assumed by many physicians that a prospective mother might have a few social drinks with negligible risk to the fetus. That point of innocuous imbibing is apparently much lower than generally believed, judging by the latest research findings. The results of a Seattle study indicate that perhaps 12% of babies born to mothers who average only a couple of drinks a day may be abnormally small, dysmorphic, jittery and tremulous — with effects later in life as yet undetermined. For pregnant women who drink very heavily, the risk of delivering an abnormal baby may be as high as 74% according to findings across the country at the Boston City Hospital." (*Medical Tribune,* New York, March 16, 1977 p. 1)

Recent studies (1977) at the University of Washington suggest that birth defects may run as high as 10% in women who have from two to four drinks a day. *Health Letter* (July 8, 1977) comments, "Normally the body slowly metabolizes alcohol. To do this it needs certain enzymes. Man is low on these enzymes. The slow rate of metabolism of alcohol is why it takes so long to recover from consuming too much alcohol and why it is fairly useless to try to speed up the process. The fetus is particularly low in the necessary enzymes which means the baby can develop very high blood levels of alcohol, much higher than the mother, and take longer to eliminate it from the fetal body. What then should an expectant mother do about alcohol? The best answer is to leave it alone."

Dr. Eileen M. Ouellette who directed the study at Boston University School of Medicine to evaluate the risk to the offspring of drinking mothers during pregnancy is quoted in the Washington Post (September 9, 1977) as saying she recommends that women give up drinking completely during pregnancy.

PROPAGANDA
Musician: "I can play better when I've had a couple of drinks."

Any musician who has played in a jazz band, a combo, a group, military band or symphony orchestra knows that precision is essential to good music. A musician that is observant can vouch for the fact that a drink or two by a fellow member will not enhance the music but will definitely break the tempo or precision.

When Guy Lombardo first organized the Royal Canadian Orchestra he set a policy he kept for over fifty years. That policy proclaimed that no member of the band could use alcoholic beverages. He pointed out that more musicians failed to arrive at the top because of the use of alcohol.

Another band leader whose orchestra has endured the years as an outstanding group has been Lawrence Welk.

Although his music is referred to as "Champagne Music," Lawrence Welk, a total abstainer, whose band is world renowned, recommends that to succeed in any profession, everyone, and especially young people, should refrain from the use of alcoholic beverages.

This band leader of almost half a century says, "As a band leader I have had numerous experiences and have developed certain convictions with regard to alcohol and music.

"In such work as mine, in which twenty musicians must cooperate, I could not afford to have one drinker nullify the efforts of the other nineteen musicians. As we play it today, music requires the utmost cooperation, sensitivity, and physical cooperation. With my various commitments, such as the weekly television show, nightly network air shows, and record and radio transcription sessions, the possibility of any drinking problem arising would be of great concern to me.

"As far as the business aspect is concerned, I am aware that one member of the band who becomes an alcoholic can ruin the musical output of the whole band, can nullify the good public relations of the group, when I need him the most, and can jeopardize my relationship with the people who hire our organization.

"Let me say that the musician who drinks the liquid liquor 'blend' can ruin the musical 'blend'." (*Listen* Vol. 8 No. 4)

PROPAGANDA

"Doctors prescribe alcoholic beverages"

In the past, as far back as the middle ages, alcohol was prescribed by doctors. However, the folklore that surrounded alcohol for medicinal purposes has vanished other than to be used as a blending agent to bind together or compound different chemicals and drugs.

Dr. Robert S. Carroll, M.D., a physician who has had outstanding results in dealing with alcoholics, has expressed deep concern about the unscientific habit of some doctors who prescribe alcohol for their patients. "Repeatedly," he says "patients lay the blame for their problem drinking at the door of physicians. I recall a score of women who claim their drunkenness was due to their doctors who counselled them to take a hot whiskey for any dozen minor ills. A large number of men were advised to keep a bottle in their desks for use when they felt let down and needed something after an attack of grippe or even a sharp cold. Numbers come to mind for who liquor was prescribed for poor appetite and, conversely, for the discomforts of indigestion,—or to fortify the patient against catching cold or picking up the flu, or regularly before the evening meal as a hypnotic for both men and women at any wakeful hour. 'Keep it at your bedside! Significantly, almost without exception these prescriptions were given by doctors who themselves were periodic drinkers. In the absence of the prescribed dose, many so professionally advised are soon to find themselves assailed by new symptoms — the crave for alcohol — more disturbing than those for which it was originally advised." (Robert S. Carroll, M.D., *What Price Alcohol* pp. 147-148).

Dr. Robert Fleming, M.D., Harvard University Medical School, who has been a specialist in alcoholic rehabilitation, tells of a woman who had arthritis of the cervical spine and "a friend suggested that she try a little brandy at bedtime; she did, and, to her surprise and gratification, the pain was relieved. She went to sleep and slept comfortably all night. If a little brandy was a good thing, more brandy was better. The result was that in time she was taking about a quart of brandy every night in order to sleep." (Robert Fleming, *Medical Treatment of the Inebriate,* in *Alcohol, Science and Society,* Lectures given at Yale Summer School of Alcohol Studies).

Dr. Carroll also puts in true focus the reason for prescribing alcohol as a medicine when he states: "Its worth as a medicine is practically nonexistent except in the eyes of those whose professional insight is tinctured with alcoholmindedness."

Are many doctors afflicted with an alcohol problem?

A two year study, published in 1977 in *The American Journal of Psychiatry,* reports that about 226,800 of America's 324,000 physicians drink, and as many as 6,000 *surgeons* in the United States are alcoholics.

If these facts are known, why do not other doctors report them to state boards of medical examiners? Dr. Robert C. Derbyshire, secretary-treasurer of the New Mexico Board of Medical Examiners says, "In many states there is a conspiracy of silence. . . . Doctors don't want to interfere with the means of livelihood of one of their fellows. Some are afraid that if they report, they'll be sued for libel."

Dr. John Duffy of the National Institute of Mental Health declares that, "The surgeon who's getting into the bottle is going to trip over his scalpel very quickly."

The late Dr. Henry W. Newman of Stanford University Medical School points out that a man weighing 165 pounds and having consumed one ounce of alcohol will show an increase of 59.7% in errors due to lack of muscular coordination. A surgeon above all medical men needs perfect coordination of his muscles.

Dr. G. Douglas Talbott who is the head of the Disabled Doctors Plan of the Medical Association of Georgia says "I know an orthopedic surgeon who was operating on a disc in a patient's back while he was intoxicated. He cut the ureter of the left kidney so badly they had to take out the kidney. . . . Another surgeon was operating on a patient's stomach while he was drunk and he nicked the major artery. They had to sew it up."

Doctors that prescribe alcoholic drinks for any physical problem are not keeping up with the many "wonder drugs" discovered in the past few years which will not give the addiction problem associated with alcohol. A twentieth century doctor who practices 18th and 19th century medicine should be avoided.

PROPAGANDA
"A drink of whiskey is good for snake bite."

Possibly the worst thing one can do is to take any alcoholic drink if bitten by a snake.

If one is bitten by a snake the natural reaction is for the body to become tense. This is good for it constricts or narrows the blood vessels. Usually a tourniquet is placed around the arm or leg to stop the flow of poison in the blood.

However, in taking a drink of whiskey the blood vessels are dialated or enlarged allowing the blood, with the snake venom in it, to flow more freely. And then to complicate the problem still further, the alcohol causes the entire body to relax thereby aiding in the freer flow of the poison.

Snake venom causes a marked fall in blood pressure. Beer, wine or liquor also lowers blood pressure.

This lowering of the blood pressure by the snake venom, plus the alcohol can be tragic to the victim. Alcohol does not neutralize the snake venom.

PROPAGANDA
"Alcohol aids digestion"

The opposite is true — alcohol retards digestion because an excessive production of mucus and hydrochloric acid due to its irritant effect on the membranes of the digestive tract.

In the book *Alcohol, Its Effects on Man,* Dr. Haven Emerson devotes a whole chapter on alcohol and digestion. He summarizes, "Alcohol in whatever amount or strength cannot properly be described as a digestant, a gastric tonic, or a stimulant to digestion. . . . Beers in small amounts have no definite effect on the digestive ferments but have in the main the same effects as red wines and sherry in retarding digestion."

PROPAGANDA
"It takes a real man to hold his booze"

Some boys seem to think that this propaganda is the criterion for judging manhood.

If being able to "hold their liquor" or to "drink everyone under the table" is the sign of manhood then the "real men" are the alcoholics found on any city "skid row."

As an individual consumes liquor there are certain percentages of alcohol that will cause a definite reaction. The average person will pass out or "slide under the table" when they have a body alcohol content of 0.4%. When the percentage reaches this level the body tries to keep the person from killing themself with alcohol and this passing out or losing of consciousness is what saves them. However, some individuals will lose consciousness at 0.35%. On the other hand the alcoholic because of alcohol destruction to his central nervous system has a built in edge on the normal person for his body alcohol content may go as high as 0.45 or 0.5% before he drops out. One would hardly consider the alcoholic a "real man."

Also, in considering this problem the body weight

of the individual enters into the percentáge problem. A man that weighs 220 pounds has almost twice as much body tissues as the man weighing 120 pounds. As the alcohol in the drink is distributed throughout the entire body the larger man must drink more to reach the same body alcohol content as the smaller man.

So the ability "to hold his liquor" contains some variables that have nothing to do with real manhood.

PROPAGANDA
"A 'stiff' drink of brandy is good for a cold."

If this were true, no alcoholic would die in the winter. However, the majority of skid-row alcoholics that die during any given year die of pneumonia during the winter months and all will have plenty of alcohol in them.

When a person consumes any alcoholic drink be it beer, wine or liquor, the alcohol causes the blood vessels to dilate and the pores of the skin open, thereby the drinker is more susceptible to contacting pneumonia.

Drinking a "hot toddy" or taking a "stiff snort" is comparable to one taking a hot bath and then standing in a cold draft.

PROPAGANDA
"Everybody drinks."

Don't you believe it! Everybody is not drinking as long as you and I are not drinking. When people make a ridiculous statement claiming everybody drinks they really mean that the people they associate with drink. On the other hand, the people I associate with do not drink, but I don't make a silly statement like "nobody drinks" just because my friends don't drink.

Who then does all the drinking?

The Consumer Data Bank of the Chicago Sun-Times/Daily News in 1968 published the following chart on men beer drinkers in the Windy City.

BEER USAGE

Daily Personal Usage	Percent of Men		Percent of Total Product Usage
Non-Users (none)	39%		12%
			26%
Infrequent Users (Less than 1 Glass)	28%		
Regular Users (1 or 2 Glasses)	19%		62%
Heavy Users (More than 2 Glasses)	14%		

Base: Chicago SMSA—Men (Brand Rating Index 1967)

Note that the "regular" and "heavy" users represent 33% of the men beer drinkers and they consumed 88% of the beer consumed. Note also that 67% of the men were non-users or infrequent users and of this group, the infrequent users consumed only 12% although they represent 28% of the men of Chicago.

PROPAGANDA
"A cup of hot black coffee or a cold shower will sober one up."

Neither a cold shower nor a cup of hot black coffee will "sober one up." A person who has been drinking alcohol must get the alcohol out of the body to be sober. This takes time. About 97% of the alcohol will be oxidized in the liver and 3% will pass out by way of the urine, pores and sweat. In either situation it is a time consuming process. The liver can oxidize about 7 to 10 grams (approximately $\frac{1}{3}$ oz.) of alcohol per hour.

Fresh air, exercise, hot coffee, cold showers or any other of a score of gimmicks used by the uninformed will do nothing to eliminate the alcohol more quickly. The rate of oxidation may vary slightly in individuals but not enough to make any noticeable difference in the sobering process.

Perhaps one of the most ridiculous techniques used by some drinkers is the one wherein the drinker thinks the alcohol will have no effect if a tablespoon of butter is taken before imbibing. Perhaps such a character thinks by "greasin' the innerds" the alcohol will go "scootin' right through."

Silly as some of these barroom ideas are to the informed person they, neverless, are seriously held and propagated by many.

PROPAGANDA

"Drinking doesn't affect my ability to drive a car."

Millions of words of cautioning regarding the problem of drinking and driving will be broadcast around the world in the days leading up to all holidays. State, federal, as well as city agencies will carry on a program of warning about highway safety; but the majority of the "action" taken by these groups is, in reality, a phony public relations pitch to let the people of the state and nation know that they are in there working for their salary. After all, isn't that what the good old taxpayer expects and for which he dishes out multiplied millions of dollars each year to keep these agencies going?

Do I sound cynical? I don't mean to be; but year-after-year we hear this same song about drinking and driving; but seldom do we ask the radio and TV stations if they are truly concerned about the problem, why then do they keep invading every home and car by radio and TV with their cleverly produced commercials, pushing the use af alcoholic products which constitute the one and only reason as to why the driver was drinking and driving.

The majority of radio and TV stations will glamorize the use of beer and drinking — seeking to make such activity the "in thing" with the youth of our nation. The reason they advertise, glorify and push drugs is the well known love of money. The media knows that advertising pays. The beer industry knows it pays to advertise. And the gullible public sits back and "soaks-up" the intellectual garbage spread out by the media; but the American taxpayer pays the bill — the bill of friends and loved ones being slaughtered on the highways, the bill of increased law-enforcement personnel to attempt to cut down the slaughter, the bill of increased auto insurance cost due to accidents and killings by the drinking driver, etc., etc., etc.

Not only do the radio and TV stations give the phony sound of concern for the highway slaughter, but the federal, state and city agencies issue statements, reports, and materials (at the taxpayers expense, of course), that are equally phoney. Take,

for example, the ridiculous attempt by some government agencies to help stem the drinking-driving
problem. One tax supported agency put out some
small, wallet-sized cards for the drinker to carry
with him to see just how drunk he is. The chart
given on the card points out that a man weighing
160 could have three drinks and still be called a
prudent driver. Where did they ever come up with
such an unscientific chart on the scale of how much
a person could drink and still not be effected in their
ability to operate a motor vehicle? This agency has
been "had" by the liquor industry. The chart idea
was developed by the liquor industry. The liquor
industry published the charts in national magazines
and the gullible leaders of some agencies and committees were used by the liquor industry to further
the philosophy of "it's OK to drink and drive, as
long as I follow the chart." Such reasoning it simon-
pure, 100%, unadulterated hog-wash; yet it is being
propagated with the taxpayers money. Undoubtedly,
these agencies have not done their homework and
research, without which they are unqualified to take
the taxpayers money and occupy a place of leader-
ship. Yet they publish an idiotic liquor industry chart
to let the public think they are working at their job.

Perhaps you are saying, "Well, I weight about 165
pounds, how many drinks can I take and still be a
safe driver?" To answer that, let me refer to the
study by Dr. Henry W. Newman and his staff at
Stanford University, who became alarmed at the
number of persons killed each year on the highways
of California by some drinking driver who always
maintain he or she only had a couple of drinks.
Dr. Newman determined that a person weighing 165
pounds, who had two drinks (beer, wine, or liquor)

would be slowed down in reflex action time by 17.6%. To be slowed down in reflex action time means just how much longer it takes a person to respond to a given stimulus. In driving a motor vehicle, that means that by the time the driver notices a pedestrian in the path of the car until he responds to this crisis situation and slams on the brakes that he will function 17.6% slower, if he has had two drinks and weights 165 pounds.

But that is not all that Dr. Newman determined. He maintained that the 165 pound person would commit 39% more errors in driving a motor vehicle, due to lack of attention, and 59% more errors due to lack of muscular coordination. How a city, state or federal agency can ignore such research on drinking and driving is hard to comprehend.

If a man or woman, weighing 165 pounds and having just a couple of drinks, will have 59% more errors due to lack of muscular coordination, what can we say for the smaller person weighing say 100 pounds? He or she would be expected to have over 90% more errors due to lack of muscular coordination. This is due to the fact that the alcohol taken in the two drinks is absorbed immediately from the stomach. The alcohol does not have to go through the digestive process, but is immediately picked up by the blood and circulated throughout all the tissues of the body. The person weighing 100 pounds does not have as much body tissue for the alcohol to be distributed through as does the 165 pounder, so he or she would have a higher alcohol content to their body and, thereby, become a better candidate to be charged with "driving while under the influence" of the drug ethyl alcohol, and, therefore a more dangerous driver.

Some of the frequenters of bars, taverns and cock-tail clubs do not like to be thought of as alcoholics or even looked upon as dangerous drivers, but the fact remains that alcohol will place them in that position, whether they admit it or not. One cannot, by his own desires, demand his own body not to become intoxi-cated. Those that think so are suffering from a bad case of self-hypnosis and self-deception. The will is located in the frontal lobes of the brain, and this is the area of the brain first effected by alcohol. That effect is anaesthetic — in other words — the brain is put to sleep by ethyl alcohol and one cannot make proper decisions with an anaesthetized brain.

The frequenter of the cocktail bar, is a problem for the highway safety people. Drinking persons cannot and will not be able to drive in a safe condition even though they may think they can. The highway slaughter will never be effectively over-come until all agencies concerned about the problem begin to tell the whole, viscous, bloody story about what ethyl alcohol does, and list it scientifically for what it is — a narcotic, habit-forming drug that does *not* stimulate the user, but rather it slows down and retards the normal functions of muscular movement and depresses the thought patterns necessary to operate a motor vehicle or to perform any normal task.

In 1899 the first American died in an auto accident. His name, H. H. Bliss. He was struck by an electric taxicab as he stepped down from a trolly car in New York City.

By 1904 drinking and driving had already become a problem and the Quarterly Journal of Inebriety carried an editorial which said, "inebriates and moderate drinkers are the most incapable of all persons to drive motor wagons."

Seventy-five years later, the same fact is stated. The American Insurance Association says flatly that, after only one or two drinks, the critical judgment of a driver and his ability to react quickly in an emergency are seriously impaired.

The results:

—Judgment is impaired.

—Inhibitions and restrains relaxed.

—Reflexes are slow.

—Vision, particularly side vision is diminished.

—A false sense of "self-confidence" increases.

—Ability to distinguish small differences in light and sound decreases.

—Muscular coordination and timing become impaired.

Any driver, regardless of age, race or sex, is a candidate for trouble if he drinks. The American Insurance Association maintains that at least three groups can be described as more accident-prone than the general population. They are young people, social drinkers and chronic or uncontrolled alcoholics. The AIA believes that the social drinker presents the biggest problem as an automobile driver. Their conclusion is based on statistics which tend to show that the social drinker outnumbers the actual drunk.

"The social drinker has the mistaken idea that a few drinks will not effect his driving ability. What's more, this type insists on driving, not realizing the extent of his impairment. In fact, in his judgment, a drink or two stimulates him to become a better driver. . . . Alcohol does not stimulate. It depresses the central nervous system, removes inhibitions and social restraints and definetely impairs the ability to drive safely. This is the so-called 'lift' which gives the impression of stimulation." (*"Whiskey at the Wheel,"* J. Marse Grant, page 73.)

The public has taken the social drinker too lightly. The people of the United States must be educated to, and must accept the fact that they cannot drink socially and drive.

In 1970 an unprecedented campaign was launched by Chicago traffic courts against *social drinkers who drive.* The crackdown resulted in a 64% drop in traffic fatalities and a 50% decrease in personal injury accidents, compared with the prior year. Fatalities during the period of Dec. 18 through Jan. 3, 1970 totaled 8 compared with 22 for the same period in 1969, — 23 in 1968 and 25 in 1967.

These startling statistics were disclosed by Raymond K. Berg, supervising judge of the traffic court, Circuit Court of Cook County, Ill. at a meeting of some 200 traffic safety coordinators.

Judge Berg said it was well publicized prior to the Christmas holidays that anyone convicted of driving while under the influence of alcohol would be sentenced to a minimum of seven days in jail coupled with a one-year's driver license revocation.

National statistics show that alcohol is involved in more than half of all fatal traffic accidents. In view of this, Chicago undertook a program, unpresedented in the United States, to develop a workable solution to this problem.

Instead of concentrating on the chronic alcoholics, as some programs do, Chicago officials decided "to "concentrate on the 'social drinker' as a major cause of traffic fatalities and accidents," Judge Berg said.

A study by the Psychiatric Institute, Cook County Circuit Court, showed that only 20% of the "driving while intoxicated" arrests are alcoholics, while 80% are social drinkers.

The study further showed that stern penalties tend to decrease the number of repeating violators in the social drinking class.

Quoting the report, Judge Berg said most social drinkers think that drunken driving laws are "made for chronic alcoholics and not for social drinkers. . . . Since these individuals are not alcoholics and since they do not get drunk in the usual sense, social drinkers get the feeling the law is not for them, saying, 'That man they're talking about is a drunk, an alcoholic, not me'."

The lesson should be clear. There is a way to cut down traffic fatalities, injuries, and accidents if the courts and the police are determined, and if public sympathy is behind them, but it can't be done by making it easier for the social drinker to drink and drive.

There is a second type of drinker who creates a big highway safety problem. This is the fellow who says "I do my drinking on the week-ends and at home — I don't touch the car all weekend."

This character will gather his 6 packs around himself and settles down before the TV for an alcohol saturated weekend. He thinks he will sleep it off Sunday night and be fit for work on Monday. He may or may not realize the hazards he faces, not just during or immediately after drinking, but during withdrawal periods. The withdrawal effects can last through Monday and Tuesday. They certainly last longer than 72 hours.

Toronto, Canada, research scientist, A. Eugene Le Blane of the Ontario Addiction Research Foundation says, "These after-effects can include significant disruption of the ability to concentrate on two things at a time — such as on the techniques of normal driving and, when suddenly, on what to do when a car pulls out of a side street. Or it can be a crane operator fastening his crane and watching nearby power lines at the same time."

The facts on drinking and driving have been proclaimed in the U. S. for over 75 years, but the process goes on — drinking — driving — killing — injuring, because the drinker in the majority of cases is an ego-centric person, who is going to have his bottle regardless of what may happen. Persons of this type are basically immature, — never fully weaned — bottle babies who maintain that they know what is best for themselves and for others also, even if it kills someone.

Some of these *drinker-drivers* may profess to be members of some church, yet they overlook the serious responsibility of every adult Christian to set an example and that the adult Christian is always to be careful lest they do anything that might cause a weaker brother to stumble.

Each year many persons make resolutions — some are kept — some are broken. Would it not be wonderful if the social drinker would make a resolution that is based on scripture. In the Book of Romans, chapter 15, Paul writes "It is right not to eat meat or drink wine or do anything that makes your brother stumble." What better resolution could someone make than to remove himself from being the stumbling block over which some other person may stumble and fall into the pit of alcoholism?

PROPAGANDA

"We need to develop a concept of responsible drinking."

The expression "responsible drinking" is a type of "double-talk" used by the liquor industry and advocates of drinking. It was even picked up by some government agencies engaged in the alcoholism problem and in particular it was promoted by Dr. Morris Chafetz when he was the director of the National Institute on Alcohol Abuse and Alcoholism. Chafetz was successful in selling the concept to many who were not very adapt in perceiving the consequences of such a philosophy.

Fortunately, the NIAAA has decided to drop the "responsible drinking" theme from its educational and public information efforts. Dr. Ernest Noble, the successor to Dr. Chafetz, at NIAAA, at a session of the Institute's Advisory Council on October 7, 1976, declared, "I don't think that the concept of responsible drinking is something we should continue because I don't know what the heck responsible drinking means—."

Where did the concept of responsible drinking come from? The liquor industry, though pushing the idea, claim they did not originate the concept. Mr. Malcolm E. Harris, president of the Distilled Spirits Council of the United States, Inc., speaking at a meeting of the Council in Miami, Florida, said, "It was the church, not our industry which developed the concept of responsible drinking. We accepted it as a good concept and we have promoted it for the past five years.

"In 1969, eight years ago, the Ecumenical Council

on Alcohol Problems published a booklet on responsible drinking. The booklet was developed by a committee of leading Massachusetts clergymen and endorsed by Richard Cardinal Cushing, Archbishop of Boston, and by major church leaders of other faiths. The booklet's basic concept focused on the normal drinker and clearly urged 'responsiblility in the use of alcohol . . . in every situation'."

When analyzing the concept any reasonable and rational person should come to the conclusion that there is no such thing as responsible drinking, but rather there are only varying degrees of irresponsibility.

PROPAGANDA

"A couple of drinks at lunch helps one work better."

Does a couple of cocktails or two bottles of beer help one do better work during the afternoon?

Dr. Henry W. Newman, Stanford University Medical School, was concerned about the tremendous highway slaughter caused by drinking drivers who claimed they "only had a couple of drinks."

Two drinks contain approximately one ounce of alcohol.

Dr. Newman conducted his experiments based on how two drinks, or one ounce of alcohol, effected a person weighing 165 pounds. He determined that:

1 oz. of alcohol retards muscular reaction by 17.4%

1 oz. of alcohol increases decision time by 9.7%

1 oz. of alcohol increase errors due to lack of attention by 35.3%

1 oz. of alcohol increase errors due to lack of muscular coordination by 59.7%

Any person having had a couple of drinks and then

returning to work can be expected to function at the slowed down rates shown above. Can any business man afford to have a secretary or office worker operate any office machine or equipment in such a condition — not drunk, but definitely error and accident prone because of lack of muscular coordination? If the secretary or office personnel weighed less than 165 pounds the percentages of retardation would be greater than those listed above. (See propaganda item "I can handle booze. Drinking doesn't affect my ability to drive.")

If a business executive has no objection to his secretary having a couple of drinks for lunch, but he is concerned about the percentage of inefficiency and error that comes from the two drinks there is one thing he can do to reduce that percentage. He should hire a secretary weighing 330 pounds and the percentage of errors will be cut by 50%.

BEER PROPAGANDA

One of the most eminent American physicians, Dr. Haven Emerson, former president of the Board of Health of New York City, Professor Emeritus of Public Health Practice at Columbia University, said of the use of beer.

"No one can take seriously the statement of the brewers proponents that 'beer is not an *intoxicating liquor.*' Beer, whether of low alcohol content, such as 3 or 4½% up to the heavy alcohol beers of England which may carry 8 and 9% alcohol, are not uncommonly used to the point of drunkenness, and the histories, medical and police records around the world are and have been for many years full of evidence that *beer and beer alone may and often is used in sufficient amount and strength to cause all degrees of drunkenness from stupor, confusion, boisterousness, brutality of conduct to unconsciousness,* but only rarely to the point of death.

"In beer-drinking countries where beer may be the only alcoholic beverage commonly used at home and at drinking places in public, drunkenness is common and easily recognized. The brewers are merely restating some of the arguments used before Congress when 'non-intoxicating' beer of 1.75% alcohol content was legalized during Prohibition.

"Ask any physician in civil or military practice and he will give plenty of instances of beer drunkenness. The records of Bellevue Hospital, New York City; of Cook County Hospital, Chicago; of Boston City Hospital, Boston, abundantly prove that drunkenness may and often does follow beer drinking without other alcoholic beverages."

In some states 3.2 beer is defined as a non-intoxicating beverage. Such laws, written by legislatures influenced by the beer lobbyists, may call beer of 3.2% non-intoxicating but scientific research has proven otherwise.

Dr. Walter R. Miles, Professor of Psychology at Yale University has given unanswerable scientific evidence of the intoxicating effects of beer as weak in alcohol content as 2.75%. Other distinguished research scientists corroborate Dr. Miles findings.

Dr. Harvey W. Wiley (*Encyclopedia Britannica,* 14th Edition) one of the best known chemists of his time said under oath "Beer containing 2.75 per cent alcohol by weight has a sufficient amount of alcohol to intoxicate the average person in quantities often consumed" (Hearings Ways and Means Committee, 72 Congress, p. 21)

Abel R. Todd, official chemist for the state of Michigan, under oath stated that "Beer containing 3 per cent of alcohol by volume (2.75 by weight) is intoxicating." (Ibid p. 24)

Dr. Arthur Dean Bevan, past president of the American Medical Association said: "There can be no doubt but that beer containing 2.75 per cent alcohol is an intoxicating beverage and that an individual can become drunk on the amount frequently consumed. (Ibid)

If 2.75 beer is intoxicating it is most certain that 3.2 beer must be intoxicating.

In experiments at the Karolinska Institute, Stockholm, Sweden tests were conducted in which experienced auto drivers were given 3.2 beer in quantity enough to give them an alcohol blood content of only .04, well under the limit allowed by Swedish law for intoxication. Nevertheless, a deterioration in driving test skills averaged between 25 and 50%.

A person does not have to reach the legal percent of .10 alcohol blood content to be a dangerous driver.

Anyone who doubts that 3.2 beer can intoxicate need only visit any saloon or tavern and witness the parade of those who as Shakespeare said have had their brains stolen away.

In 1955 beer researcher Leon A. Greenberg uttered a "hic" that staggered the boys in the back room. He claimed that beer of 3.7% could not intoxicate because the capacity of the human stomach is limited to two quarts and it would take 2½ quarts of 3.7 beer to raise the alcohol content of the blood to .15, so Greenberg claimed, "those quarts would have to be consumed in two or three hours, and this is 'physiologically unnatural'." Dr. Harry M. Tiebout, psychiatrist and vice chairman of the Connecticut Commission on Alcoholism, said "Dr. Greenberg's view is simple nonsense . . . in the eyes of most beer drinkers. They may know nothing about their blood level or the percentage of alcohol content of the beer they drink, and they care less. WHAT THEY DO KNOW IS THAT THEY GET DRUNK ON BEER, using their definition . . . Alcohol is alcohol in any concentration, and its regular use can lead to trouble."

"I do not wish to take issue with the esteemed

professor," said Ted Gunther, who is Secretary of a Local Beer Drivers Union; "nor do I wish to fault him. I can only ask in all humility whether this man of learning ever had a good load on. Any driver, any saloon keeper, — Hell, ANYBODY WHO DRINKS BEER! would most assuredly venture to disagree with the professor. I've seen men drinking beer fall flat on their faces. But maybe it was the smoke in the tavern."

Hans Grieme, proprietor of Flanagan's Place, New York City, who has served beer on two continents, said: "Beer is non-intoxicating only when it is left in the barrel."

Shortly after Dr. Greenberg's "scientific deduction" on beer not being intoxicating the California Supreme Court in a decision dated November 2, 1956, held:

"The word 'beer' like the words 'brandy', 'whiskey', 'gin', and 'rum'," is held universally to be an intoxicating liquor per se for the reason it is within the common knowledge and ordinary understanding that it is an intoxicating liquor." (Molin vs Munro, 302 Pac (2d) 818)

PROPAGANDA
"But, it's only beer."

How often this self-excusing phrase is used. Either from ignorance or misinformation this "authorative" expression is set forth as a conclusion that beer should not be classified with alcoholic drinks.

The ingredient that makes alcoholic drinks dangerous is ethyl alcohol. Its chemical formula is C_2H_5OH, and it is classified as (1) an anaesthetic, (2) narcotic and (3) toxic drug. Ethyl alcohol is basic to beer.

Perhaps some think beer is not dangerous because the percentage of alcohol is lower in beer than in wine or liquor *when considered on the volume basis*. But this is where the confusion arises. Rather than comparing liquor, wine or beer on the volume basis the comparison should be made on the alcohol per drink basis.

The standard size (1¼ ounce) liquor shot glass will contain 40 to 50 percent ethyl alcohol. Approximately ½ an ounce of the drink is alcohol. The standard wine glass (4 oz.) will contain approximately ½ ounce of alcohol. The standard beer bottle or can of beer contains 12 ounces BUT ½ an ounce of that content is alcohol.

From the stand point of *how much alcohol is consumed* it makes no difference whether a person consumes a bottle of beer, a glass of wine or a shot of liquor, for the amount of ethyl alcohol is approximately the same in *EACH* drink.

However, there are other substances in beer that should be considered, although ethyl alcohol is the "chief villain." Many do not realize that beer contains a second narcotic drug—one that is not found in liquor. For this reason many consider that beer is more addicting than other alcoholic drinks. That second narcotic drug is lupulin. It is doubtful if even one beer drinker in ten thousand knows this fact.

A recent newspaper headline stated "Young Substituting Beer for Marjuana." The article tells of a survey conducted for the Merit Publishing Co., Northfield, Illionis. It consisted of 23,000 replies from students in 18,000 of the nation's public and parochial high schools. Only 34 percent of the students said they never drank beer.

Dr. John R. Butler, assistant commissioner, Division of Alcoholism, New York Department of Mental Hygiene poses a thought provoking problem when he states that "we have become so blasé about alcohol that we tend to regard it merely as an innocuous social beverage."

Why have we become blasé? But why shouldn't children drink beer? They are "brain washed" day after day by radio, TV and all type of advertising media encouraging them to drink. And, believe it or not—advertising DOES pay.

HEW points out that over 460,000 children between the ages of 9 and 18 are alcoholics. We have a child alcoholism problem and the vast majority began their infamous journey with beer. But this should be expected for the development of this child alcoholism problem follows the sage advice of warning given in the Japanese proverb—

> "First the man takes a drink,
> Then the drink takes a drink,
> Then the drink takes the man."

To meet the issue of child alcoholism squarely we must ask "How?" and "Why?"

How did the use of beer get such a grip on the young? A great share of the blame must go to the educational (?) and mind shaping techniques of television.

The Miami Herald editorial of June 14, 1973, states the problem so vividly.

"What the TV beer commercials do not say is that beer contains America's No. 1 drug, alcohol, that alcohol is a habit-forming addictive drug, and that there is as much alcohol in an 11-ounce bottle of beer as in a one-ounce shot of whiskey.

"The masterly written commercials and the brewing industries' Madison Avenue copy mesmerizes children and creates attitudes that tend to associate sports activity with an alcoholic beverage. When 22 of the 24 major league baseball clubs have beer sponsors, how can we expect kids to separate the superb play of one of their idols from the sponsor's message that follows? The motives of the industry expressed in *The Brewers Digest* are clear: '. . . Now is the time to appeal to young people, the most logical big-volume consumer, in a way that will encourage them to remain beer drinking customers the rest of their lives'."

How did the use of beer get such a grip on the young? The beer industry was able to usurp the family circle. Catch the boys through sports and get the girls through their mothers. Preposterous? No, not as far as the beer producers are concerned. In, the booklet *The ABC of Beer Advertising* the United States Brewers Foundation, Inc., attacks the family by seeking mothers' approval of beer and ale in the home, stating that: "One of the strongest influences within the family is, of course, the mother. She is traditionally the moral guardian—the family shopper as well. Much of her time is devoted to food—planning meals and parties, picnics, get-to-gethers and entertainments. Advertising that associates beer and ale with food and family sociability is attuned to one of mother's main concerns. Beer is today largely a 'home-affair' and home means family. This is the new condition that must be kept in mind."

How did the use of beer get such a grip on the young? By television? Definitely! In January 1954, the president of the American Broadcasting Company, Mr. Robert E. Kintner, made a speech to the

U. S. Brewers Foundation at Los Angeles, California. Here are some of the quotes.

"Let me say first of all I would not have accepted your invitation if A.B.C. was not a willing servant of the beer industry. It is our 'privilege' to sell you—it is not just your 'ability' to buy us. I say that advisedly because I have sat over the period of years in meetings among our affiliates and in various parts of the country and have heard people criticize the broadcasting business, as a public franchise, for taking beer advertising. As far as ABC is concerned, we not only actively solicit it, we definitely want it; we believe it is a basic part of the American scene just like our radio and television business is. In fact, if vodka is the Russian drink, we'll take beer as the American drink because it exemplifies the difference between a free enterprise system and a communist system. So let me say that we approach your industry with a great desire, both on our local stations and on our network, to cut the pattern to fit your cloth. And may I compliment, very sincerely, The United States Brewers Foundation and its advertising agency the J. Walter Thompson Company,, for the building up by advertising and public relations of the concept that 'beer belongs' as the family drink of a freedom-loving people."

Mr. Kintner continues, *"Turning to the broadcasting business, I believe that we in radio and television also have played a part in putting beer in the home and making it the national family drink of moderation. There are no media anywhere in the country—and I do not say this in a competitive spirit—that can come in the home and talk intimately to the entire family as can radio and television, whether it be* network or local stations. And I think it is more than a coincidence that this trend towards packaged selling (which saw the percentage of beer sales shift from 75 per cent draught and 25 per cent in bottles in 1933 to the exact opposite in 1953) has increased since 1948 when the television networks began to come into dominance until today when they also blanket the country."

"If I may turn first to radio, unlike or perhaps like Mark Twain's death, the death of radio has been greatly exaggerated. There are no media within the United States or within the world that can reach more people more quickly, at lower cost per thousand, and I invite the attention of you brewers to opportunities in radio which, honestly, I do not believe have been capitalized upon.—By 'your television' I mean group listening, the entire family around the set. Radio, though, has turned into what I will call 'my radio' — more individual listening whether it be by the man, the woman, the teen-ager or the child."

"I believe that this radio trend can be capitalized upon by the brewers—

"I would suggest that even though the woman of the house may not be the deciding factor in the final purchase of the brand of beer, if she is anything like my wife, she will have something to say about it. Therefore, I believe that your agencies should consider daytime network radio; it is an extremely cheap buy. It gives millions of impressions; a constant repetition of 'go to the icebox and get a bottle or can,' or 'go to the store and buy such and such a brand.' I think this is more and more essential to the beer industry because of the change in the buying of packaged goods and the growth of self-service markets, where there is no man behind the counter to give suggestions.—

"I believe that there is a place in television for all types of brewers whether local, regional, or national; when they come to local shows, the syndicated shows or the big national shows.—"

Kintner prophesies color TV future when he states:

"Of course, the most important thing to you for the future is color. There isn't any doubt that color for beer as a brand identification, as a more effective selling tool, can be equally important to the creation of television itself.—

"However — I do not believe there is any doubt that the new electronic color will be the greatest sales medium ever invented and that it will be more effective than black and white in selling food and beer.

"Overall, I would say that the part radio and television has played in helping you in bringing beer into the home has been a part of which we are proud. We believe that these media are the proper way, the best way and the more efficient way to come into the home and tell your story, whatever the brand. And the more the story appears and is told generally, the greater is consumption. In closing I know I can speak for the entire radio-television industry when I say we are very proud to have played a small part in encouraging freedom-loving America that 'Beer Belongs'." The American Issue, September 1954.

How did the use of beer get such a grip on the young? Mr. Kintner gave the answer.

PROPAGANDA
"Beer is a food."

Occasionally one will hear someone say they have had a liquid lunch, meaning they have had a couple of bottles of beer or a couple of cocktails for lunch instead of wholesome food.

While alcohol might be called a food, it is not a complete food. Alcoholic drinks contain no proteins or fats which are essential for sustaining life. Vitamins are essential but none are found in hard liquors or those containing distilled alcohol as whiskey and gin.

Beer and wine do not contain vitamin A, D, C, or B_1 all of which are necessary for nutritional reasons. By comparison milk is a complete food. Beer has about one-half to two-thirds of the fuel value of milk as a food. The very little food value found in beer is in carbohydrate (dextrine) and a small amount of protein and a minute amount of two of the B vitamins. However, many ordinary foods contain these two vitamins in much larger amounts. So from the standpoint of a nutrition the value of alcoholic drink is practically nil.

The eminent American physician and professor, Dr. Haven Emerson, while teaching at Columbia University had conducted many research projects on all of the alcoholic drinks. Regarding the use of beer he said:

"Beer is extravagantly costly if bought for food use. It contains a moderate carbohydrate content as maltose, but no other food substance and lacks all vitamins: and furthermore, the physiological use of the carbohydrate of beer in the body is coupled with the depressant and toxic effect of the alcohol percentage present."

In working with an alcoholic the essential rehabilitation program usually begins with a multi-vitamin and mineral therapy. This, it is contended, must be done before any counseling, psychological or psychiatric program can begin. An interesting discussion of this program was given in *New Age Nutrition* (Henry Regenry, Chicago, 1974) by Dr. William D. Philpott, a behavioral psychiatrist, and should be checked by those interested in the nutritional aspects.

Dr. Roger Williams, the famous nutritional biochemist, is the foremost proponent of the nutrition-alcohol link. His research has led him to the conclusion that some people, because of their hereditary background have unusually high needs for certain vitamins and minerals. Because the need for large amounts of vitamins and minerals isn't filled by food, these unfortunate people are particularly susceptible to the lure of alcohol, which magnifies their problem rather than curing it.

Similar research on nutrition and drinking has been conducted at Loma Linda University Medical School in California and parallels the research by Dr. Williams.

PROPAGANDA
"I can tell one brand from another."

The fact is, beer drinkers cannot tell one brand from another.

A study conducted by researchers at California State Polytechnic University in Pomona experimented with 20 students, half of whom said they were devoted to particular brands of beer. The other half admitted they knew little about it. Each was given four different brands to sample without knowing which brands they were drinking.

The four beers ranged from expensive brews to low-priced local beer. The researchers reported, "Not one of the 20 could taste any difference." (*National Enquirer,* 10-14-73)

The same is true regarding drinkers of liquor, although they will argue with anyone who suggests otherwise.

The California Attorney General conducted a hearing on liquor price support programs and fair trade laws in 1974. The hearing was held in San Francisco. In the course of the testimony given, the information was brought out by an industry member that liquor drinkers favor the higher priced brands even though the bottles contained the same spirits as the lower priced bottles.

The Attorney General was informed that three bottles of vodka, identical because they come from the same vat, sell from $3.25 to $5.25 a bottle and the public prefers the expensive brand fifteen to one. The industry representative said the same situation applies to bourbon.

"If you poured almost any brand of bourbon into another bottle," he said, "I defy anyone to tell the difference. One of my best friends even apologizes to me for serving me my own liquor. It's the same as the expensive brand, but he doesn't believe it. Advertising by the big brand names has turned us all into automatons."

PROPAGANDA
"Beer is over-taxed."

As far back as the early 1950's Mr. August A. Busch, Jr., President of Anheuser-Busch, Inc., the big St. Louis Brewery, speaking at the Executives Club of Chicago complained that higher taxes and the resultant higher prices have forced a drop in the consumption of beer in the United States.

Is beer over-taxed?

To the contrary, in the majority of states beer is under-taxed when compared to the multiplicity of problems that come to the city and state from the use of beer. And in none of the states is beer over-taxed!

The state taxes on beer in 1975 were as follows:

State	Tax On Barrel	Tax On 12 Oz. Bottle
Alabama	15.50	5.0 cents
Arizona	7.75	2.5 cents
Arkansas	5.25	1.7 cents
California	1.24	.4 of 1 cent
Colorado	1.86	.6 of 1 cent
Connecticut	2.50	.8 of 1 cent
Delaware	2.00	.6 of 1 cent
Dist. of Columbia	2.25	.7 of 1 cent
Florida	9.92	4.0 cents
Georgia	10.00	4.5 cents
Idaho	4.65	1.5 cents
Illinois	2.17	.7 of 1 cent
Indiana	2.94	.9 of 1 cent
Iowa	4.34	1.4 cents
Kansas	4.65	1.5 cents
Kentucky	2.50	.8 of 1 cent
Louisiana	10.00	3.2 cents

State	Tax On Barrel	Tax On 12 Oz. Bottle
Maine	7.75	2.5 cents
Maryland	2.79	.9 of 1 cent
Massachusetts	3.30	1.0 cent
Michigan	6.30	2.0 cents
Minnesota	2.00	.6 of 1 cent
Mississippi	13.23	4.2 cents
Missouri	1.86	.6 of 1 cent
Montana	3.25	1.0 cent
Nebraska	3.00	1.0 cent
Nevada	1.86	.6 of 1 cent
New Hampshire	4.65	1.5 cents
New Jersey	1.03	.3 of 1 cent
New Mexico	2.48	.8 of 1 cent
New York	1.38	.4 of 1 cent
North Carolina	15.00	5.0 cents
North Dakota	4.96	1.6 cents
Ohio	2.50	1.5 cents
Oklahoma	10.00	3.2 cents
Oregon	1.95	.6 of 1 cent
Pennsylvania	2.48	1.0 cent
Rhode Island	2.00	.6 of 1 cent
South Carolina	22.32	7.0 cents
South Dakota	3.2%—4.00	1.3 cents
	over 3.2%—8.30	2.6 cents
Tennessee	3.40	1.0 cent
	plus 17% of the wholesale price	
Texas	4%—$5.00	1.6 cents
	over 4%—5.11	1.6 cents
Utah	3.10	1.0 cent
Vermont	7.75	2.5 cents
Virginia	7.80	2.6 cents
Washington	1.50	.5 of 1 cent
West Virginia	5.50	1.8 cents
Wisconsin	2.00	.6 of 1 cent
Wyoming	.62	.2 of 1 cent

It is interesting to note that some states still retain the beer tax rate that was set during the depression years of the 1930's. Surely this points up the power of the beer lobby in the state capitols.

The state taxes listed above are based on a 31 gallon barrel so some are led to believe that this is a great deal of tax. However, when the tax is reduced down to the bottle or can level the picture clears. Take for example the tax of $10.00 a barrel paid to the state of Oklahoma. The tax is not paid by the brewer, it is paid by the consumer even though the beer industry issues yearly press announcements claiming the tax is paid by the industry. To double this nefarious "public relations pitch" the beer industry never informs the public that the law permits the beer wholesaler to deduct 1% of the tax as a service charge. Where does this 1% go after being removed from the taxes collected? Some close to the industry believe that it is used by the wholesalers association as a "slush fund" to entertain legislators and state officials and thereby influence legislation and law enforcement.

The brewers are experts at spreading propaganda. In 1965 the editor of *The Brewer's Digest* set forth the technique of how to fight any attempt to increase beer taxes. He states,

"In the face of record sales of beer, we will claim that any more increases in beer taxes will threaten the nation with prohibition by taxation; in face of a growing incidence of alcoholism, we will claim that 'excessive taxation converts moderate beer drinkers to beverages of higher alcoholic potency' yet offer no proof in substantiation of the claim; in the face of our advertising beer as a social status symbol, we will claim that beer is being taxed out of the range of the

working man; in face of higher output per em-
ployee, we will claim that increases taxes will
reduce employment; in the face of the brewing
industry's already serving expertly as a revenue
scapegoat for other taxable enterprises, we will
propose our own novel alternatives; and back-
grounded by a bevy of press releases in which
we boast of our tax contribution to the economy
and in which our past tax payments have been
cutely translated into so many schools, hospitals,
homes for the aged, miles of highway, etc. (just
what 'the people' are demanding, according to
the politicians). we will turn Scrooge and would
ascend the politicians-responsibility to 'the people' by crying 'Enough!' Let's be honest with
ourselves, most of our arguments against increases in beer taxes are about as tired as the
legislative committees must be of hearing
them."

The beer industry talks loud and long about the
beer tax but it is purely beer propaganda. Take for
example the $10.00 a barrel tax mentioned above.
The consumer does not buy beer by the barrel, he
buys it by the bottle and this reduces the state tax
on this problem-creating drink to a mere 3 cents for
a 12 ounce bottle. A beer barrel contains 31 gallons.

In 1978, the state beer tax in South Carolina is
$23.81 a barrel or 7c for a 12 ounce bottle; Alabama
and North Carolina tax is $16.53 a barrel or 5c a
bottle; Georgia tax is $14.88 or 4½c a bottle. By way
of contrast, the state tax on a bottle of beer in some
states is less than 1 cent.

The tax on gasoline, cigarettes and many other
items are much higher than on beer. Why is this so?
Basically it goes back to the power of the beer
lobby upon the state legislatures.

To off-set the so-called tax benefit derived from

the sale of beer several items stand out. For example, the cost to the taxpayers to clean up the highway litter caused by beer drinkers.

No one would claim that all highway litter is caused by beer drinkers, but any observing person can see that the majority of refuse is beer cans and beer bottles.

PROPAGANDA
The throw-away bottle and can.

The breweries have been attacking those concerned citizens who are disturbed by waste, trash, cluttered and plugged drain ditches, and beaches made dangerous because of broken beer bottles and beer cans, and the tremendous cost to the taxpayer to pick up after the beer drinker.

The brewers love the throw-away beer bottle or can because it saves them millions each year. How? It is cheaper to buy a throw-away bottle or can than having to have the beer truck driver pick up the empty bottles at the store or tavern—unload them at the brewery—stack them, wash them and remove old labels before refilling them. Of course, the brewer doesn't care about the cost to the taxpayer to pick up millions of bottles and cans each year that are discarded along the highways.

When Lone Star Brewery was operating in Oklahoma City the president of the company, in 1961, stated that the major cost in beer is freight on the finished product and on the return bottles. At that time the cost on a six pack of returnable bottles was $1.15 and on throw away bottles 95c.

Back in the late 1950's former Gov. Craig of Indiana faced the dollar and cents cost to the taxpayer of picking up the discarded rubbish along the highway of that state. He reported to the legislature that the State of Indiana spent over $1,120,000.00 a year to pick up that discarded rubbish, and stated the Governor, " the vast majority of this rubbish consisted of discarded beer cans and beer bottles." Today it would cost several times as much.

Would this not be true of any state?

Who paid the bill? You did—the good ol' taxpayer.

PROPAGANDA

"Beer will put inches on the bust."

Norton Mockridge, a syndicated columnist writing in March 1971, told about Princess Luciana Pegna-telli, a jetsetter, who is regarded as one of the world's most attractive women. Although not always glamorous, she admits she once was nothing more than an icky blob. She began in earnest to reshape herself as she points out in her book called *"The Beautiful People's Beauty Book."*

Of course, there were some false starts, like the time a salon owner suggested she should drink a lot of beer to put inches on her rather flat bosom.

"I detested beer," she said, "but I drank it, I guzzled it. But instead of getting big breasts, I began to get a rather big behind." Beer will do it.

Alcoholic drinks help add on calories to any diet ending up with added fat around the middle, thighs and other places.

Because alcohol is a water-hungry chemical that withdraws water and moisutre from the body cells the use of it has always been frowned upon by beauty experts. A dehydrated and dry skin is not desired by most women.

The well-known columnist, Sylvia Porter reports on the "Arizona Maine Chance" one of the most famous health, beauty and reducing resorts in the world that is owned by Elizabeth Arden. If a woman wishes to use the services of this renowned "beauty ranch" they are informed that alcoholic beverages are forbidden. Why? Even the professional teams employed to help the visitor attain their beauty goal cannot compete against King Alcohol and his taking ways—such as taking away skin tone and beauty.

Nina Wilcox Putnam, author of more than twenty-five books and widely known for her magazine fiction stories wrote a cautioning article to women which was carried in "*Your Life Magazine.*" The article entitled "Women are Fools to Drink" calls alcohol the Glamour Saboteur. Ms. Putnam warns,

"No woman wants to jeopardize her beauty and there is something about alcohol which no beauty parlor can disguise. Every woman's face shows the record of even "temperate" drinking. The slight bloat which takes all the fineness out of even the prettiest features is universal. And, although I won't mention what the Demon Rum does to the figure, just don't forget that to the average woman drink is one of the most fattening things she can put into her system.

"The woman who drinks never stays well-groomed throughout an evening. She gets blowzy and usually puts her make-up on badly when she attempts to freshen it. Unfortunately, men — even drinking men — seldom lose their powers of observation in this respect even during the wee small hours of the milkman's serenade."

Rather than being a beauty agent and/or adding inches on the female bust, beer may actually help remove the breast. Check the relation of beer to cancer of the breast as given in the item *Propaganda: "What's Wrong With Just One Drink?"*

PROPAGANDA
"Beer is a real man's drink."

Those who hawk beer are interested in what the heavy beer drinker is like—is he really the man of "gusto"—the tough, rugged, independent he-man?

The president of Lerman and Van Leevwen Advertising Agency, Al Lerman, defines the heavy drinker as the one who "goes to the tavern and has six or seven beers with the boys."

Lerman, who has the Schlitz account, decided to visit bars and taverns and by personal observation determine who are the heavy beer drinkers.

According to Lerman, who is reported in the *Modern Brewery Age,* (November, 1977), the heavy beer drinker will "identify himself with his heroes, cop out on his own failures and fantasize his heroic virtues." In other words, the heavy beer drinking is a means to compensate for inadequate feelings about himself as a man. Further, Lerman contends that this inadequate feeling about himself causes the heavy beer drinker to talk more about his sports heroes than about sex.

Because of the heavy beer drinker's need to feel adequate and be "one of the boys" the beer commercials are aimed to help him identify with the sportsman—the ball player, the hunter, the boxer, etc.—and thereby fulfill his wishes and desires.

WINE
PROPAGANDA

"You see the wine when it sparkles in the cup and are going to drink it. I tell you there is poison in it, and therefore beg you to throw it away. You answer, it is not poison to me, though it may be to others. Then I say, throw it away for thy brother's sake, lest thou embolden him to drink also."

"Why should thy strength occasion thy weak brother to perish, for whom Christ died? Now, let anyone judge which is the charitable person, he who pleads against the wine for his brother's sake, or he who pleads against the life of his brother for the sake of wine?"

—John Wesley

PROPAGANDA
"God made it — didn't he?"

The fruit of the vine, or the cup that Jesus gave to his disciples at the last supper has many symbolic meanings. Matthew 26:27-29 reads:

> "And he took the *cup* and gave thanks, and gave it to them, saying, Drink ye all of it, For this is my blood of the new testament, which is shed for many for the remission of sins. But I say unto you, I will not drink henceforth of *this fruit of the vine,* until the day when I drink it *new* with you in my Father's Kingdom."

Was the fruit of the vine intoxicating wine or was it grape juice? Note that Jesus said "this is my blood of the new testament." The blood is the life giving substance of the human body. Truly, "the life of the flesh is in the blood" (Lev. 17:11). The blood carries not only life giving oxygen to every cell of the body, it also brings all the life sustaining nutrients, etc., and further it removes the waste products from the cells.

It is hard for me to understand why some theologians insist that Jesus gave his disciples intoxicating wine at the Last Supper. To do so would be to be inconsistent, for "the fruit of the vine", after undergoing the chemical change in fermentation, is no longer the life giving product of the vine but is the decayed product of the vine created by man, not by God. Non-intoxicating wine, or grape juice, is one of nature's richest source of vitamins and minerals essential to the growth and maintaining of vital health. On the other hand, the process of fermentation, or rotting and decaying, actually destroys the vital elements God created for the health and benefit of mankind.

The general content of grapes is: 2.8% albumen, 83.7% carbohydrates, 1.2% acids and extractives, and 2.3% mineral salts. Fermentation destroys 98.5% of the albumen, 98% of the carbohydrates, 47% of the acids and extractives, and 76% of the mineral salts. The life is gone.

DID GOD MAKE IT?

A recent newspaper article gives the statement of a leading clergyman endorsing the use of alcoholic beverages. The learned cleric was reported as saying: "God made it (alcohol). He made the grapes, didn't He?"

The answer sounds so pat, so clever, so learned. But a second look at the statement and question shows at least one basic fallacy. Consider the question first, "He made the grapes, didn't He?"

The answer to this question is a positive "Yes". God did create the grapevine and the vine brought forth luscious grapes—a food rich in vitamins and minerals but definitely non-alcoholic.

As long as the skin of the grape remains unbroken, as God created it and intended it for man's healthful benefit, it is non-intoxicating. However, if the skin of the grape is broken, the yeast or bacteria cells which give the grape a white dust like coating can enter the food created by God and set up their process of fermentation or decay. Alcoholic beverages are but the outcome of decay and rotting of a fruit, grain, or vegetables created by God.

Herein lies the fallacy of the statement made by the prominent clergyman when he says "God made it (alcohol)." God did NOT make alcohol—man made the alcohol. Man took the grapes, man mashed them allowing the yeast cells to come in contact with God's great and good food, man set them aside for the process of decay or death to create the alcohol.

Man however, did not have to pick the grapes, in fact, he could have ignored them and allowed them to dry on the vine until they became as hard as dried peas or stones—also non-alcoholic.

Man also could have picked the bunches of grapes and set them on a table or drying rack and allowed them to partially dry and become raisins—a fruit rich in food value, but definitely non-alcoholic.

Coming back to the original statement by the eminent cleric: "God made it (alcohol)." This is a fallacious statement. God created the elements out of which alcohol is produced but man enters in and, thereby adds an essential ingredient to the process of making or producing alcohol. This activity by man makes man the producer of alcohol not God.

This clergyman represents a certain denominational or parochial thinking which even goes so far as to use intoxicating wine in the place of the non-intoxicating wine called grape juice in observing communion. At the same time they insist that the bread used in the communion must be unleavened bread, or bread made without yeast because they claim that yeast is the symbol of impurity. To some it seems rather inconsistent to insist upon unleavened bread for the communion service and then insist that intoxicating wine be used which is made by the addition of yeast or bacteria cells to grape juice.

What dire circumstances can develop in the world when uninformed or misinformed church leaders speak in favor of cultural mores that are basically pagan and which can and will enslave multiplied millions each year.

Such blind leaders of the blind develop and recruit followers for Bacchus, the God of wine and drink, when they should be pointing men to Jesus Christ who gave his life that man might have real, abundant life each day. Such religious leaders do not lead men to real life but rather offer them the broad way which the Word of God says leads to destruction; they offer an imitation life—one built around a bottle containing an anesthetic, narcotic, toxic drug—ethyl alcohol.

Unfermented wine or grape juice is life sustaining. Fermented wine is alcoholic and paralyzes the sensibility and the contractability of the cells of the body and establishes the cellular problem of aggultination or blood sludging, which in turn kills brain cells.

Prior to 1969 those engaged in the study of alcohol and alcoholism knew that the chronic alcoholic had severe brain damage from the constant bout with the bottle, but what caused such damage was not conclusively known.

In 1969 the mystery of how alcohol deprives the brain of oxygen was solved by Prof. Melvin H. Knisely at the Medical University of South Carolina. Dr. Knisely is recognized throughout the scientific world as one of the outstanding experts in the study of blood and particularly in regard to the subject of "blood sludging or agglutination."

This eminent research scientist is very positive in his documented conclusions that even one drink kills brain cells. Under questioning, he further disclosed that the pregnant mother who sips her beer, wine or cocktails is placing in her body the toxic drug that can, by the process of agglutination, destroy brain cells within the embryo or fetus she carries.

It is impossible for this writer to accept the pleadings of some clergy who would have Jesus the Christ, the giver of real life, engage in using, endorsing or supplying to mankind a product that will destroy the highest faculty in man—his brain.

Would the one who came to give man real life have created a drink of death to man's brain at the beginning of His earthly ministry?

PROPAGANDA

"When the Bible speaks of wine it was intoxicating or fermented wine."

During the later part of the 19th century the majority of Biblical scholars seemed to agree that wine in the Scripture meant intoxicating wine. Nearly all commentaries, dictionaries, and encyclopedias of that era as well as those of modern times are in harmony with that theory. However, as concerned Christians should we accept the testimony of modern scholars if it can be shown that the making and drinking of intoxicating wine was not nearly so universal in ancient times as some would have us believe?

The Biblical question of wines is one that cannot be settled exclusively by lexicons and dictionaries. In this situation the scholar has little advantage over the ordinary reader who has common sense and education enough to determine the evident meaning of a word by the context and use to which it is applied.

Those seeking to defend the theory that all wine used was intoxicating or fermented claim the ancients had no refrigeration as we have today to preserve the grape juice in an unfermented condition. Such a claim is but to display their ignorance of the laws of fermentation. Ancient history has many references from Plato, Aristotle, Virgil, Plutarch and others who point out that there were at least four ways by which grape juice or any fruit juice could be kept in an unfermented state for upwards of 200 years. The four main ways of preservation of grape juice or "wine" in an unfermented state were:

1. *Boiling.* By boiling the water is evaporated leaving a thick syrupy liquid which would not ferment. Dr. Casper Newman, Professor of Chemistry, Berlin, 1759 said, "It is observable that when sweet juices are boiled down to a thick consistence, they not only do not ferment in this state, but are not easily brought into fermentation when diluted with as much water as they had lost in the evaporation." (*Bible Commentary*, p. 81, *Nott.*, London Ed.)

The ancients mixed their wine with water before serving. Aristotle, (384-322 B.C.), the Greek philosopher, writing about Arcadian wines said, "The wine of Arcadia was so thick it was necessary to scrape it from the skin bottles in which it was contained, and to dissolve the scrapings in water."

Pliny, (23-79 A.D.), the Roman scholar, mentioned that the celebrated Opimian wine had the consistency of honey after two centuries of preservation and storage.

Horace, (65-8 B.C.), the Roman poet, says "there is no wine sweeter to drink than Lesbian; that it was like nectar, and more resembled ambrosia than wine; that it was perfectly harmless, and would not produce intoxication."

2. *Filtration*. By filtering, the yeast is removed from the grape juice, and thereby, fermentation is prevented.

Plutarch, (46-120? A.D.), the Greek biographer and moralist, in his *Symposium* says: "Wine is rendered old and feeble in strength when it is frequently filtered. The strength or spirit being thus excluded, the wine neither inflames the brain nor infests the mind and the passions, and is much more pleasant to drink."

3. *Subsidence*. The gluten or yeast cells are heavier than the grape juice and will settle to the bottom of the vat by their own weight. If the juice is kept at a temperature below 45° fermentation will not take place and the yeast will settle to the bottom and the clear juice drawn off.

Columella, a Spanish writer on agriculture in the first century A.D., gives this recipe: "Gather the grapes and expose them for three days to the sun; on the fourth, at mid-day, tread them; take the mustum lixivium; that is, the juice which flows into the lake before you use the press, and, when it has settled, add one ounce of powdered iris; strain the wine from its faeces, and pour it into a vessel. This wine will be sweet, firm or durable and healthy to the body." (Bible Dictionary, Nott. London Ed. p. 213)

4. *Fumigation*. Fermentation may be stopped by the use of substances containing sulphur. This was done by the use of sulphur fumes or by mixing in the juice of the yolk of eggs or other substances containing sulphur.

Adams in his *Roman Antiquities*, on the authority of Pliny and others, says "that the Romans fumigated their wines with the fumes of sulphur; that they also mixed with the mustum, the newly pressed juice, yolks of eggs, and other articles containing sulphur. When thus defaecabantur (*cleansed*, from defaeco, 'to cleanse from the dregs'), it was poured into smaller vessels or casks covered over with pitch, and bunged or stopped up."

THE OLD TESTAMENT

Hebrew is a language rich in synonyms. For example, it has over one hundred words for "take", thirteen for "man", and for the word "wine" there are eleven Hebrew words which make various distinctions and shades of meaning. It is not the intention here to have an extensive canvass of all these Hebrew words. However, since the testimony of the Hebrew Bible revolves mainly upon three of these words and their meaning, it is here attention will be given.

YAYIN—is found one hundred and forty-one times in the Hebrew Scriptures. It is a generic word and stands for the juice of the grape whether fermented or unfermented. This is wherein the chief problem lies and it is the main source of all the confusion regarding the Bible wine-question. If the word YAYIN always stood for one specific type of juice of the grape there would be no question regarding the translation. But such is not the case. Note the following texts which are but a few which show the different connotation placed upon the word *yayin*; sometimes having divine favor and other times disfavor.

Genesis 9:21: "Noah drank of the wine and was drunken."

1 Samuel 1:14: "How long wilt thou be drunken? Put away thy wine."

Isaiah 5:11: "Woe to them that continue till wine

inflame them.''

1 Samuel 1:24: "Hannah took little Samuel and a bottle of wine to Shiloh.''

2 Samuel 16:2: "Wine for such as be faint in the wilderness.''

The only reasonable explanation of this seeming inconsistency is that the word *yayin* is a general term used for all kinds of beverages produced from the vine, whether fermented or unfermented.

When the writers of the Scriptures seek to make a distinction that the grape juice is either intoxicating (fermented) or non-intoxicating (unfermented) they usually resorted to two other Hebrew words.

(1) The word *TIROSH* is used for *unfermented* wine. *TIROSH* is used thirty-eight times in the Hebrew Bible. It is never the cause of, nor is it ever associated with, drunkeness. Its use is never prohibited but always commended. It is constantly associated with wheat, corn and oil. *TIROSH* occurs in the Hebrew Bible in the following places.

Gen. 27:28: "Therefore God give thee plenty of corn and wine.''

Gen. 27:37: "With corn and wine have I sustained thee.''

Num. 18:12: "The best of the oil and the wine and the wheat.''

Deut. 7:13: "He will bless thy land, thy corn, thine oil, thy wine.''

Deut. 11:14: "That thou mayest gather thy corn, thine oil and thy wine.''

Deut. 12:17: "Eat the tithe of thy corn, thine oil and thy wine.''

Deut. 14:23: "Thou shalt eat the tithe of thy corn, of the wine," etc.

Deut. 18:4: "Give the first fruits of thy corn, of thy wine and of thine oil.''

Deut. 28:51: "Shall not leave thee either corn, wine or oil."

Deut. 33:28: "Fountain of Jacob upon a land of corn and wine."

Judges 9:12: "Wine which cheereth God and man."

2 Kings 18:32: "Will take you to a land of corn and wine."

2 Chron. 31:5: "First fruit of corn, wine, oil and honey."

2 Chron. 32:28: "Storehouses for the increase of corn and wine and oil."

Neh. 5:11: "And of the corn, the wine and the oil."

Neh. 10:37: "Fruit of all manner of trees, of wine and of oil."

Neh. 10:39: "Of the corn, of the new wine and of the oil."

Neh. 13:5: "The tithes of the corn, the new wine and the oil."

Neh. 13:12: "Tithe of the corn, the new wine and the oil."

Psalm 4:7: "Gladness more than when corn and wine increased."

Prov. 3:10: "Thy presses shall burst out with new wine."

Isa. 24:7: "The new wine mourneth, the vine languisheth."

Isa. 36:17: "Land of corn and wine, of bread and vineyards."

Isa. 62:8: "Give thy corn and thy wine to thine enemies."

Isa. 62:8: "The new wine is found in the cluster a blessing."

Jer. 31:12: "For wheat, for oil and for wine."

Hos. 2:8: "I gave her corn and wine and oil."

Hos. 2:9: "I will take away thy corn and thy wine."

Hos. 2:22: "Earth shall bear the corn, the wine and the oil."

Hos. 7:14: "Assembled themselves for corn and wine."

Hos: 9:2: "The new wine shall fail."

Joel 1:10: "Corn wasted, wine dried up, oil languisheth."

Joel 2:24: "The fats shall overflow with wine and oil."

Joel 12:19: "Behold, I send you corn and wine and oil."

Micah 6:15: "Shall sow but not reap; tread sweet wine but shall not drink."

Hag. 1:11: "Drouth upon the corn, wine and oil."

Zech: 9:17: "Whoredom and wine [*yayin*] and new wine [*tirosh*] take away the heart."

This points out that *yayin* and *tirosh* are not the same although both are from the same source — grapes. However, some may claim that only alcoholic drinks take away the heart, but we know from the Bible and from everyday experience that even things that are good can take the heart away from God. For example a farmer may find no time for God because of his crops or cattle; the city dweller because of his swimming pool, race boat, golf, travel trailer, etc.

2) The word SHAKAR (sometimes written *shechar, shekar*) refers to the liquid or juice from dates and other fruits (grapes excepted) or from certain grains as barley, millet, etc., which were dried and mixed with honey. As either type contained sugar they could become alcoholic, but both could be kept in an unfermented state by one of the four preservation methods.

The word SHAKAR is found forty-two times in the Hebrew Bible: twenty-three times as a noun, and nineteen times in the verb form.

SHAKAR is usually translated *strong drink*, and nowhere in the Bible does this word enjoy divine approval as the name of a beverage. The following texts confirm this.

Lev. 10:9: "Drink not wine nor strong drink." Wherever in Scripture this expression — "wine and strong drink" — is found, the Hebrew terms invariably are *yayin* and *shakar*.

Num. 28:7: "Cause the strong wine to be poured out."

Deut. 29:6: "Neither have ye drunk wine nor strong drink."

Judges 13:4: "Drink not wine nor strong drink."

Judges 13:14: "Neither let her drink wine nor strong drink."

1 Sam. 1:15: "I have drunk neither wine nor strong drink."

Prov. 20:1: "Wine is a mocker, strong drink is raging."

Prov. 31:4: "Not for the king to drink wine, nor princes strong drink."

Judges 13:7: "Drink no wine nor strong drink."

Prov. 31:6: "Give strong drink to him that is ready to perish." This is an opiate, anesthetic, or medical prescription; not a beverage.

Isa. 5:11: "Woe to them that follow strong drink."

Isa. 5:22: "Woe to the men that mingle strong drink."

Isa. 24:9: "Strong drink shall be bitter to them that drink it."

Isa. 28:7: "Priests and prophets have erred through strong drink."

Isa. 29:9: "They stagger, but not with strong drink."

Isa. 56:12: "We will fill ourselves with strong drink."

Micha 2:11: "Lying spirit prophesy wine and strong drink."

Num. 28:7: "Strong wine for a drink offering."
　　(Offered, not to be drunk.)

The proper understanding of these three Hebrew
words is imperative to the Bible-wine question. A
further classification of these three words is found in
the testimony of the Septuagint, the Greek version of
the Old Testament. The Septuagint sets forth the
following facts.

(1) YAYIN is uniformly rendered in the Greek
OINOS. YAYIN is the Hebrew generic term for all
kinds of wine, whether fermented or unfermented
OINOS is the Greek generic term for all kinds of
wine whether fermented or unfermented.

(2) TIROSH is the Hebrew name for unfermented
wine and the Septuagint renders it also with the
Greek word oinos, except once (Isaiah 65:8). The
Greek language has no specific word for unfermented
wine, therefore the word OINOS is used which includes everything in the nature of a beverage from
the vine.

(3) SHAKAR which is usually translated as
"strong drink" in English was never once translated in the Greek Septuagint with OINOS. That fact
alone should settle the question that TIROSH and
SHAKAR do not represent the same kinds of wine.

The Septuagint supports the thesis that:

1. The Hebrew term YAYIN is the name for all
　grape beverages whether fermented or un-
　fermented.
2. The Hebrew term TIROSH is the term for
　unfermented wine.
3. The Hebrew term SHAKAR is the term for all
　fermented and intoxicating liquors.

THE NEW TESTAMENT

In the New Testament we find the Greek word *OINOS* is the one word we have to deal with, while in the Old Testament it was mainly the three Hebrew words with different connotations. The Greek word *OINOS* stands for all the products of the vine. *OINOS* is used to translate the Hebrew *yayin* and *tirosh;* however, it is never used to render *shakar* — the word for intoxicating wine—the presumption is therefore created that *oinos* in the New Testament should never stand for fermented wine for the translators of the Septuagint never used *oinos* to translate *shakar.*

The question is often asked, "Did Jesus make intoxicating wine?" Was the *oinos* he created intoxicating or non-intoxicating?

The inquirer should ask of himself a few simple questions, such as: Would Jesus as a devout Hebrew make a drink that the Hebrew Bible condemns and prohibits?

Would Jesus, attending a wedding create 60 or more gallons of intoxicating wine which wine has a history of breaking up more families than any other item?

Then consider Paul's recommendation to Timothy to "drink a little wine for thy stomach's sake." Was it fermented or intoxicating wine which some commentators say Paul suggested for Timothy's ulcers? Hardly, for alcohol would only irritate the condition, while, on the other hand unfermented grape juice is one of the richest sources of vitamins and minerals and very beneficial to many gastro-intestinal problems.

The question regarding some of the newer translations of the Scripture often arises. Why do some

translators or those that para-phrase the scriptures
not make a clearer translation and intepretation.
Some modern translators have done this. The eminent British translator of the Bible, Ferror Fenton,
has done a most commendable job. One wonders why
some of the most highly publicized "modern translations" have failed to see some of the evidence that
substantiates the position of abstaining from the
use of all alcoholic beverages. To abstain from intoxicating drink is the solemn injunction throughout
the Bible.

A detailed and exhaustive study of Bible wines is
found in Dr. William Patton's book "Bible Wines:
or Laws of Fermentation and Wines of the Ancients."
This book can be obtained from SANE Press, 101
N.E. 23rd Street, Oklahoma City, Oklahoma 73105.

PROPAGANDA
"Brandy, wine, sherry enhance cooking."

Should alcoholic beverages be used in cooking? So
often recipes are given in newspapers and magazines
listing brandy or some other liquor as one of the
ingredients. Is there any harm in such cooking
and baking?

There are problems here in that the average person knows so little about alcoholic drinks. One may
see the liquor bottle in the store and notice that it is
usually brown, amber or ochre in color unless it
happens to be vodka which is usually clear as water.

Ethyl alcohol, or ethanol, is colorless and odorless.
An alcoholic beverage contains materials other than
ethanol and water. It is the combination of these
materials which are derived from the fermentation
and subsequent processing that gives each beverage

its unique color, aroma and taste. These materials are better known as fusel oil congeners and include acetaldehyde, formaldehyde, ethyl fromate, ethyl acetate, methanol, n-propanol and iso-anyl alcohol.

It has only been in the past few years (since 1970) that any concerted research was begun on fusel oils. Some researchers believe these congeners or fusel oils play an important part in cancer as they are not burned in the body metabolism process, and they are toxic, as Haggard and Jellinek pointed out in the 1940's.

If one uses alcohol in cooking the ethanol or ethyl alcohol will undoubtedly evaporate but the fusel oils will remain. Perhaps "cancer pudding or cancer cake" may have an appeal to some but the health conscious individual would avoid this clever sales pitch that is encouraged by the liquor industry to increase sales.

The editor of the "Woman's Page" or "Women's Section" of any newspaper or magazine is well acquainted with the many recipes that are sent to her by the public relations departments of the beer, wine and liquor industry. Of course, each recipe encourages the use of alcohol to be served as a drink or to be used in preparation of the food.

In other words, the beer, wine and liquor promoters have placed the Ladies Editor of every newspaper and magazine on their "sucker-list." The liquor industry lets the editor and newspaper sell any gullible housewife on the idea that their cancer causing product will make the food taste better? How naive are some editors and readers.

PROPAGANDA

"Americans need to learn how to drink like the Italians who have no alcoholism problem."

"If only the people in the United States would drink the way people do in France, we would have no problem." This is the argument that used to be given to favor moderation. Then came Mendes-France, his campaign for milk instead of wine in school children's lunch buckets, and the clear revelation of the immensity of the problem of alcoholism in France, and use of this illustration ceased.

Then people started saying, "If only the people in the United States would drink the way the people do in Italy, we would have no problem." And then came Professor Giovanni Bonfiglio, President of the Italian Institute of Alcoholism, in an address to the Italian Automobile Club as reported in "Alert," a publication of the International Temperance Association. Dr. Bonfiglio said:

"The importance of the damage done by alcoholism in Italy is still underestimated by the general public, by doctors, and especially by administrative authorities. . . .

"Drinking is heavier in Italy than in most of the rest of Europe and many other parts of the world. As far as Europe is concerned, Italy is second only to France. But the trend of consumption, and also to the various diseases induced by alcoholic intoxication, shows the possibility that Italy might take this somewhat undesirable record away from France, leaving to Italy the dubious glory of being the record holder. In France the situation has been realized, studied, and combatted, whereas in Italy everyone has been lulled into security by the unfounded and fallacious illusion that alcoholism does not represent a pressing problem there.

"It is evident that in the span of twenty-one years (1941-1961) consumption of wine rose 100 percent, consumption of beer 200 percent, and that of spirits 400 percent. . . .

"One cannot but expect an increase of illnesses of the clinical types resulting from the use of alcoholic drinks. . . . Statistics compiled from national surveys have shown that first admissions for alcoholic psychoses have increased 200 percent from 1947 to 1961. . . .

"In addition to the fact that they are becoming more frequent, alcoholic psychoses have shown another significant trend. The persons most affected no longer come predimonantly from the country but rather from the big towns, above all, from those where there is the greatest industrial development. A rise has also been seen in female alcoholism, especially in the regions and towns where more women go out to work and particularly where they are employed in factory work. There is also a definite trend for alcoholic psychosis cases to develop at much younger ages than in the past. . . ."

Dr. Bonfiglio continues, "All these facts are enough to discredit the old opinion that wine as an alcoholic drink is far less damaging than spirits. Both in Italy and France, where the greatest part of alcohol consumed is in the form of wine, higher figures are found both for the incidence of alcoholic psychoses and for hepatic cirrhosis of alcoholic origin than in countries such as the United States where the most wide-spread form of consumption is of spirits, or drinks with a high alcohol content. Actually, although the consumption of hard liquor has been increasing for some years now, almost all the cases of alcoholic psychoses found in Italy are due to wine. . . ."

In the July 1977 issue of *The British Journal of Addiction*, Drs. G. Bonfiglio, S. Falli, and A. Pacini, the authors of a report on alcoholism in Italy, point out a strange situation. Though alcoholism has been endemic in Italy for centuries, it is on the one hand highly tolerated and considered part of the traditional culture, and on the other hand it causes accidents and diseases and is counted as a vice. The authors state: "The dimensions of alcoholism in Italy is alarming but unfortunately no studies on the subject on a national scale are available." Two kinds of alcoholism are prevalent in Italy: the "traditional Mediterranean", which results from daily drinking, usually without overt intoxication; and the "northern and Anglo-Saxon" type, caused by neuroses or psychopathies and characterized by the use of distilled spirits. The Mediterranean type often leads to relatively early dementis and liver cirrhosis; the Anglo-Saxon type is characterized by serious behavioral disorders and active psychotic episodes.

Bit-by-bit as evidence is accumulated in every part of the world, it becomes clearly established as fact that the consumption of any kind of alcoholic beverage in any amount, in any situation, by any person, is inseparably connected with a proportionate amount of problem drinking. While there is no predictability as to which individual from a group of drinkers will become the alcoholic, the sufferer of cirrhosis of the liver or some other physical ailment, the immoral or criminal one, or the drinking driver, it is true nevertheless that a certain proportion of people who drink will develop into these kinds of problem drinkers. It is equally true that it is possible to determine in advance which people will not become an alcoholic — those who abstain from drinking ethyl alcohol.

The World Health Organization has a Sub-Committee on Alcoholism. Concluding a five year study, Dr. Robert Fleming pointed out that *"Nobody is immune to alcoholism* — it affects some persons quicker than others. . . . Most alcoholics are not psychiatric cases. They are normal people whose drinking has caught up with them. . . . Total abstinence is the only solution to alcoholism."

PROPAGANDA
"Drinking is not a moral issue."

The medical and scientific evidence proving that even one drink kills brain cells had ramifications beyond the physiological — it brought out the moral aspects of drinking. If a person consumes a product that destroys the highest faculty within the human body that person has made a moral decision whether or not he or she will admit such.

The Bible points out that the body of the Christian is the temple of the Holy Spirit. (1 Corinthians 6:19). Alcohol destroys the brain cells, causes retardation, hypoglycemia, cirrhosis, cancer — all destroying "the temple of the Holy Spirit."

Not only is alcohol detrimental to physical health but it removes moral restraints, deadens moral responsibilities and destroys spiritual fervor.

The courts of our nation see a constant stream of young men and women come before them who committed some heinous crime after having had "a couple of drinks."

The courts have repeatedly called the selling, buying and use of alcoholic products a moral issue.

"Liquor in its nature is dangerous to the morals, good order, health and safety of the people and is not to be placed in the category with the ordinary commodities of life." (U.S. Supreme Ct. Crowley V. Christensen, 136 US 86 and 137 US 83)

Dr. Roy L. Smith, former editor of the Christian Advocate, stated it clearly when he said, "There is no social, moral, or religious value which the church is endeavoring to build up that the liquor business is not tearing down. It is robbing men of their sense of value, their moral discrimination, their sensitiveness to social responsibilities, their consciousness of divinity and concern for righteousness."

PROPAGANDA
"You can't legislate morals."

This meaningless phrase is heard whenever some proposed legislation is brought before the state legislature or U.S. Congress that would in some way seek to restrict the sale of alcoholic beverages. The person using such a statement always does so with the air of finality and leaving the impression that the proposed legislation is unsound because it has a moral basis.

Is the law to be without a moral or ethical basis? One of the great jurists of America was Oliver Wendell Holmes who heard this ridiculous propaganda statement and said, "The law is the witness and external deposit of our moral life. Its history is the history of the moral development of the race. The practice of it, in spite of popular jests, tends to make good citizens and good men."

If it were not for morals the law of the jungle would reign supreme. Whenever a society downgrades or seeks to destroy the moral values found therein there is a corresponding rise in civil infraction, crime and the code of the jungle as can be seen in the 1970's.

A strong element in the development of a moral climate is seen when the legislature or congress as representatives of the people, enact restrictive legislation, for it places the state on one side or another in that specific issue. The purpose of legislation was not to set a moral standard but to restrain individuals and groups from committing immoral and anti-social acts.

The advocate of restrictive liquor laws and strict law enforcement does not expect to make bad people good by legislation, but rather the goal sought is the restraining of the unprincipled, money-hungry liquor traffic in order to provide the best possible environment for present and on-coming generations.

PROPAGANDA
"The preachers and the churches shouldn't get involved with liquor issues and politics."

The liquor traffic keeps insisting that ministers should not discuss political issues and questions in the pulpit.

In the state of Oklahoma in a Liquor-by-the-Drink

Election in 1976 the liquor industry tried to keep the churches from taking an offering to help the "dry" organization Sooner Alcohol-Narcotics Education in the battle against the liquor industry.

The court case tied up the *dry* funds temporarily but a second court released the injunction and the churches were able to take offerings to combat the wealthy liquor interests.

Should ministers discuss politics in the pulpit?

Politics is nothing more or less than the science of government. Bible students know that Romans 13:1-7 speaks of government and the duties of citizenship. The first verse says, "Let every soul be subject unto the higher powers. For there is no power but of God: the powers that be are ordained of God." The word, *powers*, can also be translated *governments*. Actually, Paul is saying we should be loyal to the government of God, and he further states that God is the author of all civil government.

If God is the author of government, the minister has a perfect right to discuss the science of government in the pulpit. As the command was given to the preacher of old, so it should be to the preacher of the present, that his duty is to be a watchman for God: "Son of man, I have made thee a watchman unto the house of Israel: therefore hear the word at my mouth, and give them warning." (Ez. 3:17)

If God is the author of civil government he surely wants righteous government. This, then, requires righteous men to administer such a government for Romans 13:3, 4 describes their duties, "For rulers are not a terror to good works, but to evil. . . . For he is a minister of God to thee for good." Because we want rulers that are a terror to evil works for the good of the people, we "for this cause pay ye tribute" or taxes. We pay taxes to have righteous government administered by good men for the benefit of all the people and as "a terror to evil doer."

Do the bar and tavern people, the gambler and racketeers, stand in terror because of any state legislature or city council? If they are not in terror then it seems evident that the government officials elected by the people are not in league with God.

Why are the evil forces in power at the state capitals and at Washington? Probably because they are united and organized to get their greedy goals while the moral forces are not united for the purpose of political action.

In Luke 19:11-13 the parable of the rich ruler is given and the ruler commands his servants to "occupy until I come." In the parable the rich ruler is symbolic of Christ and the servants are symbolic of the servants of Christ. The command given by the Savior to his followers is to "occupy" or "inherit" this world until He comes. In other words, have governments that are a terror to the evildoers and minister to the people for good.

The preacher is set as a watchman to warn the people. Yet there are those who would shackle the watchman. They don't want them to discuss politics — righteous politics — God's politics. How can such a minister educate his people in God's laws? He must choose who he will serve — God, or some man, woman, men or women or group in his congregation.

Involvement in liquor issues, liquor legislation, liquor law enforcement seems to center to a greater degree in the theologically conservative churches. The conservative churches have had a long history of deep convictions and concern about drinking and the pastors have not hesitated in proclaiming such is sermons on the Christian witness and life. Undoubtedly this concern has had a definite effect upon the habits of the members of these churches. A study conducted in 1969, entitled *American Drinking Practices, A Natural Study of Drinking Behavior and Attitudes* throws some interesting light on the effect of the theological beliefs of individuals as to whether or not they drink. The report of the *Second Special Report to the U.S. Congress on Alcohol and Health* (p. 12, 1974) states that the *American Drinking Practices* survey "revealed that there were relatively high proportions of drinkers and heavy drinkers among Catholics. Although Jews had the lowest proportion of abstainers among the three major religions, they had a very large proportion of light drinkers and the lowest proportion of heavy drinkers. Liberal Protestants showed a pattern rather similar to that of Catholics in proportions of drinkers, except that there were fewer heavy drinkers among liberal Protestants. Conservative Protestants had the largest proportion of abstainers and the lowest proportion of heavy drinkers when the four groups were compared."

"The 1972-74 surveys indicate that the same basic relationship exists among the three major religions, but there appeared to be an increase in both light and moderate drinking among Jews and Catholics. The proportions of Protestants in these categories have remained about the same since 1965."

LAWS, RIGHTS, TAXES &
THE LIQUOR CONGLOMERATES

PROPAGANDA

"Liquor is legal and should not be restricted under our free-enterprise system."

This claim of the liquor industry is a half-truth and therefore confusing to some.

The legality of manufacturing, selling and buying alcoholic products is not the same as the legality of other products. The legality of beer, wine and liquor is a RESTRICTED LEGALITY. These products can only be manufactured by those who have received a license.

These products can only be sold on certain days during certain hours. These products *cannot* be sold on certain days (Sundays, Holidays, election days, etc.); or sold to certain people (as mental patients, alcoholics, persons under the age of 21 in most states); or sold in certain places (as near churches or schools, etc.).

The courts have repeatedly pointed out the difference between the liquor traffic and other business. For example the Supreme Court of the State of Connecticut, in a unanimous decision written by Associated Justice E. A. Ingals (July 10, 1953) stated: ". . . the liquor traffic is a source of danger to the public which is not inherent in other businesses . . . there is a vital difference between intoxicating liquor and other goods affected by the Interstate Commerce Clause."

The beer, wine and liquor business IS a business but it is an unlawful business which may exist only as a result of specific, permissive legislation and under strict controls. The U. S. Supreme Court has stated: "There is no inherent right in a citizen to sell intoxicating liquors. . . . It is not a privilege of a citizen of the state or a citizen of the United States." (Crowley vs. Christensen 137 U.S. 86; 11 Sup. Ct. 13)

The United States Supreme Court Reports Vol. 34, Page 807 states:

"The United States Supreme Court has ruled that for the sake of 'public health and welfare' the states can pass and enforce laws 'that discriminate against or impose special burdens on activities and persons involved in 'the traffic in intoxicating liquors within their borders' and such power is unfettered by 'the commerce clause or the equal protection and due process clauses of the Federal Constitution'."

Again, on the right to sell beer, wine or liquor, the U. S. Supreme Court stated:

"The privileges and immunities of citizens of the United States are privileges and immunities arising out of the nature and essential character of the national government, and granted or secured by the Constitution of the United States, and the right to sell intoxicating liquors is not one of the rights growing out of such citizenship." (Bartemeyer vs. Iowa, 18 Wall. 129. See also Giozza vs. Tierman, 148, N. S. 657 (1892); Mugler vs. Kansas, 123 U. S. 623, 659 (1887)

Some of these decisions are quite old, nevertheless, they are still up-to-date and binding until some similar court reverses or contradicts them.

PROPAGANDA

"I have a personal right to drink and to sell liquor."

The liquor crowd are quick to pick up the phrase that any restriction in the sale of liquor is trespassing upon their personal liberty or rights. "Personal liberty" and "personal rights" are catchy but meaningless phrases that have been overworked. No man has the personal liberty to do as he pleases unless he is alone on an island like Robinson Crusoe. However, even Robinson Crusoe lost his personal liberty when his man Friday appeared on the scene. My personal right ends where your personal right begins.

When men seek prohibition of the sale of alcohol they do not violate the personal rights of anyone. To favor a law which forbids the manufacturing and selling of the drug ethyl alcohol does not destroy a person's rights, but rather it is promoting a policy that will guarantee to every man, woman and child the largest possible sphere of human rights. This sphere includes among other things the right to bring up children in a world free of the addicting drug — ethyl alcohol; the right to be free from the tax burden brought on by the sale of alcoholic drinks; the right to travel the highways of our nation without the fear of being involved in an accident caused by a drinking driver; the right to have one's home free from the invasion of beer and liquor advertising.

Civilization itself is founded upon the principle that personal rights must everywhere and always be relinquished for the public good.

Drinking and selling liquor is not a personal fundamental right. The United States Supreme Court stated that "There is no inherent right in a citizen to sell intoxicating liquors. . . . It is not a privilege of a citizen of the state or a citizen of the United States. . . . By general concurrence of opinion of every civilized and Christian community, there are few sources of crime and misery to society equal to the dram shop. . . . Statistics of every state show a greater amount of crime and misery attributable to the use of ardent spirits obtained at retail liquor saloons than any other source. . . . (Crowley vs. Christensen 137 U. S. 86 and 137 U. S. 83).

The courts also have determined that the right to consume alcohol is far from fundamental. "Right to consume alcohol is not fundamental, is not explicitly or implicitly guaranteed by the constitution and is specifically made subject to restriction and regulation by the Twenty-First Amendment" (Houser vs. State of Wash, 540, P 2d 412; Randles vs. State, 206 P 2d 1209).

Why should "personal rights" always be personal rights for the drinker? Does not the abstainer also have "personal rights"? Does not the non-drinker have a personal right to raise a family in a community free from the many sociological problems revolving around the drinker-highway safety problems, welfare problems, aid to dependent children problems, property devaluation due to nearness of bars and taverns, crime problems, law enforcement problems, etc?

PROPAGANDA
"Eighteen-year-olds should be allowed to buy liquor."

Several studies on the problems of maturing have cautioned against the use of alcohol by children and young people. These have been based on the accepted thesis that the average person does not fully mature until they are about 25 years of age.

Insurance companies are concerned about the young and immature driver and for this reason the insurance rates are extremely high until the driver becomes 26 years of age.

The maturing process revolves around the development of a small but vital organ located in the brain. This organ, known as the hypothalamus, is vitally effected by alcoholic beverages be they beer, wine or liquor.

The eminent Dr. Jorge Valles, M.D., a psychiatrist extensively involved in therapy work with alcoholics and vitally concerned as to "what causes the alcoholic" points out in his book *"From Social Drinking to Alcoholism"* that:

"The younger the age at which an individual starts to ingest alcohol, the greater the chances that he will develop into a chronic alcoholic. For the action of the alcohol is channeled directly toward the adolescent's imbalanced hypothalamus and autonomic nervous system, thereby obstructing his emotional maturation on both psychological and physiological levels. The regular or frequent ingestion during adolescence may produce a permanent imbalance of the hypothalamus and a concomitant irreversible malfunctioning of the autonomic nervous system, thereby leading to the development of chronic alcoholism. In brief, the direct action of the alcohol on the hypothalamus produces chronic alcoholism."

The liquor traffic in its constant pushing to lower the age for the sale of liquor keep saying that the 18 year old must be given all his rights. Such sophistic reasoning may sound plausible although it is actually fallaceous. The courts have repeatedly ruled that the "Right to consume alcohol is not fundamental, is not explicitly or implicitly guaranteed by the constitution." (U. S. C. A. Constitutional Amendment 21)

There are many "rights" that an 18 or even a 21 year old cannot claim. Because of their age they cannot hold any of the following positions.

1. President of the United States (must be 35)
2. Vice-President of the United States (must be 35)
3. A member of congress
   A U. S. Representative (must be 25)
   A U. S. Senator (must be 30)
4. A member of the Supreme Court

On the state level the following positions cannot be held by the 18 to 21 year old in the state of Oklahoma. The majority of states have similar provisions.

1. Governor of the state (must be 31)
2. Lt. Governor of the state (must be 31)
3. Secretary of State (must be 31)
4. State Auditor (must be 31)
5. Attorney General (must be 31)
6. State Treasurer (must be 31)
7. Superintendent of Public Instruction (must be 31)
8. State Examiner and Inspector (must be 31)
9. A member of State Senate (must be 25)
10. A member of House of Representatives (must be 21)
11. A State Corporation Commissioner (must be 30)
12. A District Attorney (must be 28)
13. State Bureau of Investigation Agent (must be 25)

PROPAGANDA
"The liquor taxes are a benefit to the nation."

In 1974 the Department of Health, Education & Welfare issued a report on alcohol's economic drain or cost to the nation. When all the expenses to the city, state and nation for alcohol caused problems were analyzed the picture showed the American public paid $3.18 for every $1.00 of liquor taxes received in 1971.

In 1977, a report prepared for the National Institute on Alcohol Abuse and Alcoholism (NIAAA) which covered the year of 1975, the research team of Berry, Boland, Smart and Kovak show that the economic loss due to alcohol problems in the U. S. now amounts to $4.41 for every $1.00 received ir collected liquor revenue.

To give a clearer picture note the total public revenues received in 1975 as reported by the Distilled Spirits Council of the U. S.

ALCOHOLIC BEVERAGE REVENUE IN MILLIONS

	Spirits	Wine	Beer	Total
Federal	$3,943	$199	$1,316	$5,459
State	2,159	332	1,315	3,806
Local	191	39	191	420
Total	$6,293	$570	$2,822	$9,685

The total revenue taxes of $9.6 billion makes good propaganda for the liquor industry. However, the 1975 cost of alcohol problems amounted to $42.7 billion, or $4.41 cost for every $1.00 of taxes received. The figures below, which show the various alcohol cost related problems, are from the NIAAA report mentioned above.

1975 PUBLIC REVENUE FROM ALCOHOLIC BEVERAGES

Federal	....	$5,459,000,000
State	....	3,806,000,000
Local	....	420,000,000
		$9,685,000,000

1975 ALCOHOL-RELATED EXPENSES

Lost Production	$19,640,000,000
Health and Medical	12,740,000,000
Motor Vehicle Accidents	5,140,000,000
Violent Crime	2,860,000,000
Social Responses	1,940,000,000
Fire Losses	430,000,000
	$42,750,000,000

LOST PRODUCTION

Lost production is critical amongst alcohol dependent persons. Most of the costs are intangible. Here are a few:

1. Decreased production due to tardiness and absenteeism.
2. Decreased production due to hang-over and fatigue.
3. Cost of accidents while at work and caused by drinking.
4. Scrap losses due to faulty decisions and operating procedures.
5. Medical costs for injury while at work.
6. Pension costs including premature disability and death.
7. Loss in training new personnel.

All of the seven intangibles must be absorbed by business and industry. Of course, to "be absorbed" means to add to the cost of operation, which in turn is passed on to the consumer or user of the articles, commodities, or services offered by the business or industry.

As the average alcoholic loses 22 working days a year, and considering the multiplicity of problems that come with the alcoholic when returning to work, it is easily understood why industry and business are interested in the alcohol problem. The $19.6 billion loss each year can never be regained.

Estimated National Health Expenditures as a Result of Alcohol Abuse in 1975, According to Type of Expenditure

Type of Expenditure	Total Adult Population Expenditures	Expenditures Resulting from Alcohol Abuse	Expenditures Resulting from Alcohol Abuse As A Percentage of Total Expenditures
Health Services and Supplies:			
Hospital Care	$ 42,300,000,000	$ 8,400,000,000	19.9%
Physicians' Services	17,900,000,000	1,300,000,000	7.3%
Dentists' Services	6,200,000,000		
Other Professional Services	1,700,000,000	120,000,000	7.3%
Drugs and Drug Sundries	8,900,000,000	280,000,000	3.2%
Eyeglasses and Appliances	2,000,000,000		
Nursing Home Care	8,800,000,000	190,000,000	2.2%
Expenses for Prepayment and Administration	3,900,000,000	780,000,000	19.9%
Government Public Health Services	2,500,000,000	390,000,000	13.1%
Other Health Services	3,000,000,000	330,000,000	13.1%
Construction: Medical Facilities	6,100,000,000	780,000,000	13.1%
Training and Education	2,300,000,000	170,000,000	7.3%
	$105,600,000,000	$12,740,000,000	12.1%

HEALTH AND MEDICAL

The researches at NIAAA point out that the $12.7 billion cost for health and medical care revolve mainly around the diseases, illnesses and problems associated with alcohol abuse — alcoholism, cirrhosis of the liver, heart disease, cancer, pneumonia, stomach and duodenal ulcers. The table on page 92 shows the computed costs determined by the NIAAA researchers.

MOTOR VEHICLE ACCIDENTS

Alcohol related motor vehicle accidents amounted to $5.1 billion, the third largest economic cost due to alcohol. The drinking driver is impaired in vision, hearing, coordination, judgments and tends to take risks.

In addition to the cost of the drinking drivers accidents, there is another item that must not be overlooked and that is the increased cost of automobile insurance the non-drinker must pay because some drivers claim they have a "right" to drink.

VIOLENT CRIME

The report indicates that alcohol is frequently associated with certain violent crimes such as murder (67%), aggravated assault (30%), forcible rape (24%).

The estimated cost of violent crime was placed at $2.8 billion. However, no cost figures were given for unreported crime and property damage which might have been associated with alcohol.

SOCIAL RESPONSES

The $1.9 billion estimated as social responses was determined as follows:

Estimated Costs of Social Responses To Alcohol Problems

Social Welfare System	$1,273,800,000
Alcohol Programs	74,700,000
Highway Safety Programs	29,200,000
Fire Losses	392,000,000
Criminal Justice (non-violent crime)	170,100,000
TOTAL	$1,939,800,000

Social Welfare System

$1.2 billion cost specifically due to alcohol abuse. This included (1.) Unemployment compensation programs, (2.) Public assistance programs providing income maintenance, (3.) Special emergency income relief, (4.) Workmen's compensation programs, (5.) Other Special Welfare and Social Service Programs.

Alcohol Problems

This includes expenditures for alcohol and alcohol-ism-related programs, including diagnosis, treatment, rehabilitation, prevention, education and research.

Highway Safety Programs

This item lists the economic costs due to loss of life, personal injuries, property damage, and cost of highway safety and fire protection programs.

Fires Losses

The estimated fire losses includes loss of property, loss of production from premature death and personal injury, and medical costs.

Criminal Justice (non-violent crime)

The alcohol related crime costs included a percentage cost of correctional institutions, police, courts. The report indicated that alcohol is frequently associated with certain violent crimes such as homicide, assault, and rape.

The NIAAA researchers admit their estimates are on the conservative side. This conservative estimate listing an economic loss of $42.7 billion should challenge every taxpayer to take a closer look at the liquor industry who constantly keeps propagandizing about the $9 billion liquor tax.

Anytime a business would spend $4.41 to make $1.00, that business is threatened with bankruptcy. No less can be said about a nation that condones such an economic drain.

ADDICTIVE vs. NON-ADDICTIVE

Many persons may be interested to know that some makers of distilled spirits, wines, beers and other alcoholic beverages, plus certain cigarette and tobacco manufacturers also market many food and other consumer products. For your information, the following lists have been prepared showing the addictive items on the left and non-addictive items on the right.

RAPID-AMERICAN CORPORATION

The largest single contributor to corporate revenues was Schenley Industries (p. 166 - Advertising Age 1977)

Addictive	Non-Addictive
Schenley Industries	Cross Country clothes
Schenley Reserve	Leed's Travelwear
I. W. Harper bourbon	McCrory, McLellan, H. L.
DeWar's White Label scotch	Green, J. J. Newberry and Cassels
	United retail chains
Dant, Dickel, Ancient Age, Old Charter, Long John whiskies	
Coronet brandy	Lerner shops
Samovar Vodka	Economy Auto stores
Plymouth Gin, etc.	Oklahoma Tire & Supply Co.
	Botany 500, Wonderknit clothing
Imported wines, Dubonnet, MacNaughton	Talley House restaurants
	Holland House

AMERICAN BRANDS

Addictive

James B. Beam Distilling Co.
  whiskeys and wines
Bell's and Spey Royal scotch
Dark Eyes Vodka
Beameister wines
Pall Mall, Tareyton, Silva
  Thins, Maryland, Carlton
  and Lucky Strike cigarettes
Rio-Tan Cigars, American
  Cigars

Non-Addictive

Sunshine Biscuits
Duffy Mott items
Grandma's Molasses
Clamato juice, Beefamato
  juice
Acme Visible Records
Jergens cosmetic products
Master Locks
Swingline staplers, etc.
Acushnet golf items

HUEBLEIN, INC.

Malcolm Hereford Cows
Smirnoff Vodka
Hamm's Beer
Italian Swiss Colony Wine
Don Q rum
Bali Hai and Key Largo Pop
  wines, etc.

Kentucky Fried Chicken
A-1 Sauce
Snap-E-Tom tomato cocktail
Grey Pompom mustard

NORTON-SIMON, INC.

Canada Dry Bourbon, gin,
  vodka
Somerset Importers
Johnny Walker Red scotch
Johnny Walker Black scotch
Crawford's scotch
Pedro Domecq cognac,
  brandies, tequila, etc.
Old Fitzgerald Bourbon

Avis Car Rental
Hunt-Wesson Foods
Hunt sauce, tomato paste,
  ketchup, tomatoes
Hunt's Snack Pack
Wakefield seafood
Reddi Whip
Barrelhead root beer
Canada Dry ginger ale,
  mixers, etc.
Max Factor cosmetics
McCall Patterns
McCall Publishers
McCall Magazine
Orville Redenbachers
  Gourmet popping corn
Redbook
Wesson Oil

STANDARD BRANDS

Addictive

Fleischman's whiskey, gin, vodka
Royal Vodka
Old Canada Canadian whiskey
Fleischman's bourbon
Benedictine liquers
Souverain-California wines
Bollinger champagne
several brands of wine

Non-Addictive

Blue Bonnet and Fleischman's margarine
Planters Nut products
Chase and Sanborn coffees
Tenderleaf tea
Curtiss Candy items
Baby Ruth, Butterfinger candy
Egg-Beaters
Royal gelatin desserts and puddings
Standard Brands
Chemical Industries, industrial products
pet foods

LIGGETT AND MYERS

L&M, Chesterfield, Lark, Eve cigarettes, also smoking and chewing tobacco
J&B Scotch Whiskey, Wild Turkey Bourbon, Grand Marnier brandy, Catto's Gold Label Scotch, Royal Ages Scotch, Izmira vodka, Austin, Nichols and Co., liquors, importers of various wines

Eve Fashion clothing
Superstar games and sporting goods
Alpo and Alamo dog food
Liv-a-snaps
National Oat Co., Cream of Oats, 3 Minute popcorn, 3 Minute Oats
Pepsi Cola Bottling Co. of Fresno, California

PHILLIP MORRIS

Miller Highlife Beer
Philip Morris, Benson & Hedges, Parliament, Virginia Slims, Multi-filter cigarettes
Revelation tobacco

American Safety Razor Co.
Personna blades
Clark Chewing gums
Milprint packaging
Nicolet's Spec. papers
Polymer chemical products

NATIONAL DISTILLERS AND CHEMICAL CORPORATION

Old Crow, Old Taylor, Old Grandad whiskies
Gilbey's gin
Vat 69 Scotch
Bourbon Deluxe, etc.

U. S. Industrial Chemicals
Bridgeport Brass (Revere Copperware)
Beacon Manufacturing Co., upholstery
Inwood Knitting Mills, dress fabrics

PREVENTION
&
REHABILITATION
PROPAGANDA

They are slaves who fear to speak
For the fallen and the weak;
They are slaves who will not choose
Hatred, scoffing and abuse
Rather than in silence shrink
From the truth they needs must think.
They are slaves who dare not be
In the right with two or three.

—James Russell Lowell

The parental attitude toward drinking is most important in shaping the child's use or non-use of alcohol.

If parents want their children to abstain from the use of alcoholic products, two requirements will be required: (1) total abstinence on the parent's part and (2) parental disapproval of drinking.

The question of parental example and disapproval of drinking was vital enough for the authors of "Drinking in Colleges", (Bacon and Strauss), to make a study of the matter. On page 100 is a tabulation of their findings. They questioned drinkers, non-drinkers, moderate drinkers and alcoholics, as to the attitude of their parents toward the use af alcoholic beverages.

So often factual studies that might effect the liquor industry are never given much publicity, but are buried away in technical journals. We give this revealing summary in the hope that it will encourage parents to speak up, as well as abstain from America's most abused drug.

ATTITUDE OF PARENTS OF NONDRINKERS TOWARDS
THE DRINKING OF ALCOHOLIC BEVERAGES

Father's Attitude Toward Drinking	Non-Drinking Male College Students	Non-Drinking Female College Students
	(Percent)	(Percent)
Abstaining and disapproving	77.8%	75.9%
Abstaining, not disapproving	5.6%	5.2%
Moderate occasional use	8.8%	8.6%
Moderate regular use	1.8%	1.0%
Occasional intoxication	1.8%	4.0%
Heavy drinker	1.8%	2.9%
Alcoholic	1.4%	1.0%
Unknown	1.0%	1.5%

Mother's Attitude Toward Drinking	Non-Drinking Male College Students	Non-Drinking Female College Students
	(Percent)	(Percent)
Abstaining and disapproving	97.2%	94.3%
Abstaining, not disapproving	1.1%	2.4%
Moderate occasional use	1.1%	2.0%
Moderate regular use	—	—
Occasional intoxication	—	—
Moderate regular use	—	—
Heavy drinker	—	0.4%
Alcoholic	—	—
Unknown	0.7%	1.0%

Note especially that those abstaining but not disapproving did little to influence their children.

Another study comes from the Department of Psychiatry, University of Washington School of Medicine, and published in the Quarterly Journal of Studies on Alcohol (Vol. 14 p. 596) deals with the "Attitudes of the Parents of Alcoholics, Moderate Drinkers and Non-drinkers Toward Drinking." "Non-drinkers tended to come from homes in which neither parent drank and where both parents disapproved of the use of alcohol, suggesting that they have developed an attitudinal structure which excludes the drinking of alcoholic beverages from the range of permissible behavior for themselves. Alcoholics, on the other hand, tended to come most frequently from homes in which one parent drank, usually the father, who made the use of alcohol moderately and occasionally."

The December 1977 Gallup Poll survey on teenage drinking points up the crucial fact that teen drinking level is linked to views of their parents.

Mr. Gallup says, "A key reason that alcohol abuse among U. S. teenagers has reached such frightening proportions is seen in the fact that as many as one-fourth of parents do not have any rules or guidelines regarding the use of alcohol by their teenage children.

The biblical formula still works: "Train up a child in the way he should go: and when he is old, he will not depart from it." (Proverbs 22:6)

The Christian witness is paramount in shaping the future. A witness, to be effective, must not only be vocal, it must be seen in the life of the one witnessing.

PROPAGANDA

"An alcoholism rehabilitation program must not stress total abstinence."

Practically every state and large city has a council, committee or agency who are tremendously interested in the alcoholism problem. These groups are to be encouraged IF they realistically face the alcohol problem. However, all too often these councils fall into a situation similar to what took place in Wisconsin several years ago. The Wisconsin State Journal carried a story head-lined, "Doctors Urged to Help Fight Alcoholism," which said, among other things:

"The help of doctors and the general hospitals must be enlisted in the fight on alcoholism in Wisconsin, spokemen for groups interested in the problem agreed at a meeting here Wednesday.

"Formation of a specific program for the State Bureau of Alcohol Studies must wait until a permanent director of the unit is named, they said.

"Director John Tramburg of the Department of Public Welfare said he was asking for an examination, limited to Wisconsin residents, to fill the post.

"Tramburg said that his department's search for a new bureau director is being limited to State residents 'because it is important to understand Wisconsin traditions' on the use of liquor.

"Wisconsin people traditionally have had something to drink in their homes; it's a part of the family ritual in many cases,' he said. 'They like their glass of beer or wine at the table, and a lot of them had it during Prohibition.

"'Liquor sales are legal, and we have to learn to live with it. We're not interested in someone to promote Prohibition.'"

If they are not interested in prohibiting the sale of the narcotic drug — ethyl alcohol — they are then bureaucrats perpetrating a fraud on the citizens of the state. The blundering of bureaucrats serves but one purpose — to keep themselves at the public feed trough.

The fallacious reasoning of Mr. Tramburg is seen in his narrow vision which is limited to say the least.

He leaves the impression that *all* Wisconsin people drink and *all* Wisconsin homes have alcoholic drinks in their homes. What he should have said is that he and those he associates with are drinkers — but rather, because of his own personal choices he places everyone in that same category which is false reasoning. There are hundreds of thousands of Wisconsin people who do not drink because of religious and moral reasons and therefore find they are not dependent upon an anaesthetic, narcotic drug to enjoy life.

Dr. Joy Elmer Morgan, former editor of the Journal of the National Education Association stated it so clearly when he said, "Drinking in moderation is not the solution to our liquor problem. It is the main cause of that problem."

Who are the "do-gooders"?

This group is composed of individuals similar to the above mentioned bureaucrat as well as social workers, clergy, etc., who claim they are so concerned for the alcoholic that they want to force him into an alcoholic rehabilitation program.

The forced commitment "binge" that is currently sweeping across our nation is basically the outcome of bureaucratic desire for a bigger slice of the taxpayers dollar and a perpetuating of "the system". The concern for the ultimate help to the alcoholic is purely secondary if it is considered at all.

The forced commitment alcoholic rehabilitation program has been tried in several instances but after experimenting with their theories the promoters usually find their original task had been multiplied several times. This increasing of problems revolves around the psychological buildup of hostility the forceably committed alcoholic developes toward those who have had him institutionalized — the spouse, the doctor, the judge. Before any effective alcohol "rehab" program can be undertaken the alcoholic's resentments, frustrations and anger against the "do-gooders" must be resolved.

An example of bureaucratic bungling of the alcoholism problem was seen when Maurice E. Chafetz, M.D. was the director of the National Institute on Alcohol Abuse and Alcoholism. Chafetz asserted, "It is the task of the practicing physician to take the initiative in acting to provide adequate medical and follow-up care for alcoholic persons." When he calls giving physicians the power to imprison alcoholics, a "Bill of Rights" for the alcoholic we have a perfect illustration of bureaucratic double-talk or gobbledegook.

The eminent psychiatrist, Dr. Thomas S. Szasz, writing in the British medical journal, Lancet, as an academican and teacher challenges Dr. Chafetz, stating:

"I believe our duty now is to stand up against . . . 'Chafetzism' or the 'Crusade Against Alcoholism and Addiction' or to call it by some other catchy phrase hardly matters; what matters is that as physicians and teachers we resist politically motivated and mandated redefinitions of bad habits as diseases; that we condemn and eschew involuntary medical and psychiatric interventions; and that, instead of joining and supporting the "holywar" on alcoholism and drug abuse, we actively repudiate this contemporary version of 'popular delusion and crowd madness'." (*Lancet*: 7-8-72)

There is no doubt that the popular delusion is that

alcohol is a necessary ingredient in our society. Chalk one up for the public relations arm of the liquor industry. Not only must the medical profession repudiate this popular delusion but the clergy must realistically face up to the fact that too often they have compromised the Biblical command to "Look not thou upon the wine when it is red, when it giveth his color in the cup, when it moveth itself aright." (Proverbs 23:31)

Even a grade school student should know that Proverbs 23:31 refers to wine when it has fermented or "moveth itself aright." But do they? Where would they learn such? — In school? — At home? — In church?????

As for the alcoholic can he find deliverance from his "bad habits"? Many do. Jerry J. Dunn in his book *God is for the Alcoholic* says, "I am an alcoholic. I know what it is like to burn with a desire to drink that is so overpowering that family, job and friends mean nothing. . . . I also know the joy of deliverance from the power of alcohol addiction." Dunn not only talks about the alcoholic and his problems, but he provides a clear-cut Christ-centered solution.

So often the "do-gooder" rehabilitation expert forgets that man is also a spiritual being and in so neglecting this side of man his high-geared, highly financed and costly "rehab" program comes to naught.

PROPAGANDA
"Alcoholism is a disease."

A theory is a theory — is a theory — is a theory. Concerned students of alcohol and alcoholism problems must always remember that the disease theory of alcoholism is just that — a theory. Webster's dictionary defines "theory" as "speculation, presumption." The disease theory is a speculation that has been around for over one-hundred years.

However, the disease theory received little consideration until the Yale School of Alcohol Studies picked up this theme and by use of pseudo-scientific statements, the promotion of an alcohol-excusing physiology, and use of the mass media propaganda of the wet press, the theory has been accepted by the unquestioning do-gooders as documented scientific fact. They published a volume for teachers entitled, *Alcohol and Social Responsibility* which on page 216 tells the reader that an emphasis leading to total abstinence and presenting the dangers of drink is unsatisfactory.

For almost forty years the Yale School of Alcohol Studies philosophy has been pushed by the liquor interests. The liquor industry has constantly poured money into the research conducted by this group. It is small wonder that many of the champions of social drinking have been pushing the drink cult philosophy as a repayment of the scholarships supplied by the liquor industry through the Distilled Spirits Institute and DISCUS, the Wine Institute and the United States Brewers Foundation.

One example of this loyalty to the alcohol industry is seen in an address by Dr. Leon A. Greenberg, Director of the Yale School of Alcohol Studies laboratory. Addressing the convention of the United States Brewer's Foundation and reported in full in *The Brewers Digest* (February, 1958 p. 41ff), Dr. Greenberg assured his audience, the Brewers,

". . . the research currently going on and the studies planned for the future . . . I believe can contribute significantly to the welfare of your industry."

No valid objection can be made to any university doing an endowed research on any subject or substance if the study begins and continues without personal prejudices on the part of the researcher. However, any research that is done with the purpose of learning the "constructive" role of that substance, such as beer, and not giving equal time and effort to the "destructive" role places that "scientific research project" in the category of a propaganda endeavor. But, of course, the Yale School of Alcohol Studies has never been classed as a neutral scientific research agency, so anyone seeking factual and unbiased research must study each project from this school with a very candid, searching and critical approach.

Dr. Ernest Gordon in *Wet Science Invades the Schools* (page 105) raised the question as to the "leanings" of the Yale School of Alcohol Studies when he wrote, "Is the credibility, as well as the respectability, of Yale School of Alcohol Studies compromised by the $90,000 brewery money given it by Mr. Rahr? When the donor of this considerable sum and the receiver of it, the Director of the Yale School, were both asked if it represented a collective gift from various brewers, no reply could be elicited. But is not the public entitled to know this in view of the farflung invasion which the Yale School is undertaking in our public school system? Also, in view of the fact that Yale School management has categorically denied ever receiving any liquor money?"

The Yale School of Alcohol Studies philosophy and

tactics if discussed in detail would require several volumes. However, if the reader cares to read a scholarly and documented treatices on the subject he should read *Alcohol Reaction at Yale,* and *Yale Alcohol Science Tested in Thirteen Documented Briefs,* both by Ernest Gordon. Dr. Albion Roy King in his volume *Basic Information on Alcohol* also gives an excellent analysis of the disease theory.

When the Yale School sent out the volume Alcohol and Social Responsibility in 1949, the assistant surgeon-general of the United States Public Health Service is quoted on page 142 as affirming that alcoholism is America's No. 4 Public Health Problem; and 750,000 persons are classified on page 82 as chronic alcoholics with 3,000,000 more listed as inebriates.

Thirty years later the Department of Health, Education and Welfare maintained that alcoholism is America's No. 1 public health problem and the U. S. has 9 million alcoholics plus 10 million inebriates. Is not 30 plus years of Yale-Rutgers philosophy enough to arouse the American public as to the fallaciousness of this liquor industry propaganda. It is readily noticeable to the critical researcher that the Yale-Rutgers theoreticians are quick to rebut any idea, book, magazine article or scientific research project that would give discomfort to the liquor industry. Any effort on the part of citizens to restrict in any way the sale of alcoholic beverages is promptly denigrated by the followers of the Yale-Rutgers philosophy. And the press is too often subservient to the liquor industry because of advertising income. Too often the press becomes subservient to the liquor industry because the publication of scientific reports might effect the sale of the liquor industries products. So the public goes on — uninformed; and the liquor industry goes on — creating alcoholics.

Is alcoholism a disease? If it is, as the disease theory propagandists contend, why do they insist that alcohol has nothing to do with the disease? If alcohol has nothing to do with alcoholism, it seems quite evident that the disease should not be called alcoholism.

When the discussion of alcoholism is lead by a sociologist he invariably will stress the sociological problems he feels have contributed to create the alcoholic — such as poverty, poor housing, unemployment, race discrimination, etc.

On the other hand, the physiologist tends to see the alcoholism problem revolve around physical and health problems, under-active or over-active glands, or certain other physiological problems which may be biological and inherited.

The psychologist usually sees within the victim such problems as frustration, worry, fears, anxieties, etc., which must be removed to return the person to normalcy.

The psychiatrist is often inclined to look for some abnormal or deviant behavior, often inherited, as the cause of the alcoholics problem.

It's very interesting to notice that the untrained non-professional members of Alcoholic Anonymous, the Salvation Army, the Rescue Missions and the conservative churches are doing a better job in helping the alcoholic return to society than all the professional groups combined.

Over the years I have met scores of persons who were poor, unemployed, discriminated against, physically suffering, frustrated, fearful, and had some emotional abnormalities, but they were not alcoholics because they didn't drink alcohol.

Some so-called "professional workers with alcohol" will undoubtedly charge the above statement as being an oversimplistic analysis. But why should we have to make the alcoholism problem so complicated — except, perhaps, to create another state department or agency to be operated by some do-gooder who usually talks in complicated terms but basically does little or nothing in the area of rehabilitation except offers excuses based on "not having enough money to do the job."

Drinking may cause one to become ill but illness in the ordinary sense of the word is not a disease.

In the prestigious British medical magazine *Lancet*, the eminent psychiatrist, Dr. Thomas S. Szasz, Professor of Psychiatry, State University of New York, Upstate Medical Center, Syracuse, N.Y. gives a refutation to the claim that alcoholism is a disease. He, out of concern for the alcoholic states: "Excessive drinking is a habit. According to a person's values he may consider it a good or bad-habit. If we choose to call bad habits 'disease', there is no limit to what we may define as 'disease' — and 'treat' involuntarily. The misuse of alcohol — whatever the reason for it — is no more an illness than is the misuse of any other product of human inventiveness, from language to nuclear energy."

Edward J. McGoldrick, Jr. was the director of Bridge House, an agency for the rehabilitation of the male alcoholic in the New York City Department of Welfare. The McGoldrick method of alcoholic rehabilitation has been one of the most successful in the

United States and is outlined in his book *Management of the Mind,* and was twice written about in Readers Digest. Speaking with deep concern for the alcoholic he says: "The greatest hindrance to prevention, rehabilitation, cure, therapy, counseling, and help to the alcoholic is: to subsidize the drinking of alcoholics by telling them that their conduct is due to an illness. This, to my mind, is spiritual and psychological sabotage."

He continues, "The excessive drinking of the alcoholic is no more a disease than stealing cars, bad temper, resentment, jealousy, drug addiction, selfishness, prejudice, or a host of other irresponsible habit patterns of reaction . . . those vagaries of conduct so typical of all of us.

"These blocks to successful living can be removed as they were erected — by the use of the mind — by radical changes in mental attitudes, the cause of behavior.

"My twenty years' experience in this field, consisting as it does of helping thousands of alcoholics from all walks of life, constrains me to emphasize with all of the vehemence at my command, how essential it is for members of the medical profession, social workers, clergymen, judges and others dealing with the alcoholic, to discard once and for all this dogma of sickness. Let's get hold of our common sense, sit back and reflect upon what undoubtedly most of us already know but have been a bit careless in applying: that an orderly, responsible and decent society is based upon the indispensable premise that individuals are self-accountable and self-responsible for their behavior; that this behavior is instinct with ethics and morality. Why, then insist on mouthing what appears to be a vested interest piece of propaganda, which redounds ultimately to the ruin of a fellow human being?

"To say that alcoholics are sick is only part and parcel of that kind of thinking that insidiously gnaws away at the principle of personal responsibility by allocating the blame for anti-social behavior to the myth of "illness."

"Let all of us, when we meet with this sickness dogma, dispel this propaganda fog and look at this alcoholic for what he or she is — pitiable and pathetic, certainly — a flop and a failure, actually. And not a person to be coddled or wet-nursed, but a fellow human being who has been avoiding the psychological pains of life by resorting to the artificial heaven of a drug and, consequently, indeed purposefully, acquiring and establishing a habit pattern of addiction."

Another psychiatrist, Dr. Jane N. Higbee, says: "In my years of dealing with mental and emotional problems, I have found that treatment of alcoholics is frustrating and usually less than successful. It is my belief that nothing less than placing the responsibility for drinking squarely upon the shoulders of the individual involved, is the only sensible step in approaching the problem."

If alcoholism is a disease, it is the only disease that is bottled and sold across the counter. It is the only disease that requires a licensed store to spread the disease. It is the only disease that is advertised and glamorized on radio, TV and movies. It is the only disease the government taxes. It is the only disease that is habit forming. It is the only disease in which researchers have been unable to find a germ or virus.

Somewhere on the road to rehabilitation and restored dignity, the alcoholic must accept responsibility for himself.

PROPAGANDA
"Almost all Jewish people drink but they have no alcoholism problems."

Moderationists, some so-called "scientific" and educational groups, and the liquor traffic have for years promoted the idea that the Jewish people have fewer problems with alcohol than do religious bodies which teach abstinence. The purpose of this propaganda item is an attempt to make the teaching of abstinence seem as unsuccessful in avoiding alcoholism and even causing alcoholism.

Theodore Greenhood, who for 27 years was the secretary of the Jewish Temperance Association in Boston, was very concerned about what he considered the distorting of Jewish drinking to promote the consumption of alcoholic beverages. In an article entitled "Jews Resent Being Used to Promote Moderation", Mr. Greenhood said, "The fact that ritual wine is used universally by the Jews and the fact that relatively few Jewish alcoholics are seen have been twisted together to form an argument used in teaching the 'moderate' use of alcoholic beverages, and used against education for total abstinence."

Mr. Greenhood belonged to a Reform Temple, but he has also attended Orthodox and Conservative Temples on an average of four times a week. He gives some interesting information not known to many outside the Jewish faith:

"According to my conception, Jews, as a rule, do not drink in moderation. Rather we consider ourselves to be total abstainers. Because we do use small amounts of wine, symbolically, in our centuries-old religious observances, many of our Christian friends might not believe that we may properly be classified as total abstainers, but we are much more—particularly the Orthodox Jews —total - abstainence - minded than moderation-minded.

"The only person who is qualified to report on our Jewish drinking customs would be an active member of one of the Jewish congregations, not survey teams out to prove a point in a few 'question and answer' visits."

He points out that except at religious services the "Orthodox Jews do not otherwise drink at home—at all. They do not drink at breakfast, they do not drink at lunch, they do not drink at supper, they do not drink between meals, not even a mouthful of wine. They do drink water, tea, coffee and milk, not only at meals but at all hours, but never any spirits, and no wine except symbolically in religious observances."

"Purely secular rituals such as graduations, weddings, etc., are sometimes utilized for drinking purposes by some members of the 'reform branch' of the Jewish religion."

"I can write, as a Jew, that we Jews practice a certain form of oriental face saving and we do hide our drunks and our alcoholics (those who have left the path of Jewish total abstinence, as we see it and have attempted to travel down the non-Jewish road of moderation)."

"It is time the Jews protest being misused as symbols of successful moderate drinking; rather they are true symbols of foes of 'moderate' and excessive drinking. The practice of moderate drinking by Jews inevitably leads to a considerable number of us becoming drunkards and alcoholics."

"They may not be in the public eye as much as comparative unfortunate Gentiles, but we have drunkards and alcoholics in equal numbers—numbers of Jewish moderate drinkers coming to grief compared to numbers of Gentile moderate drinkers who come to grief."

The fact that the Jews do follow what Mr. Greenhood calls "oriental face saving" has been pointed out numerous times by researchers. Schmidt and Popham in "Impressions of Jewish Alcoholics" (Journal of Studies of Alcohol 37:931-939, 1976) wherein they determined three patterns were discernible in the way the patients perceived of themselves as alcoholics and as Jews. One way the study points up is that those with a non-orthodox background accepted their diagnosis of alcoholism but denied their "Jewishness." This denial of their Jewish background would help account for the popular but baseless belief that Jewish people have no alcohol problem.

Because alcoholism is a growing problem amongst their people, the Federation of Jewish Philanthropies has organized a Task Force on Alcoholism for the Jewish community in the New York City area.

THE PROHIBITION ERA

More than 125 years ago, Lord Macaulay, the great English essayist, historian and statesman wrote prophetically of the United States:

"Your Republic will be pillaged and ravaged in the 20th century, just as the Roman Empire was by the barbarians of the fifth century — with this difference, that the devastators of the Roman Empire, the Huns and the Vandals, came from abroad, while your barbarians will be the people of your own country and the product of your own institutions."

PROPAGANDA VS. FACT

Why re-hash an old argument? Why stir up past history? Why not let dead issues lay?

Concern causes one to re-hash, stir-up, and probe for truth.

No subject has been more lied about, propaganized against and misrepresented than has the subject of "The Prohibition Era."

Those engaged in the manufacture and sale of alcoholic beverages become panicky when anyone suggests that additional controls are needed over that industry. They immediately cry out that any control, no matter how minor is a "return to Prohibition."

The liquor industry and those they have deceived by propaganda claim over and over and over again that Prohibition was

1. A disastrous time of crime, lawlessness, etc.
2. A failure.
3. Rejected by the people.

What are are facts?

You the reader can make the choice whether you will accept propaganda or fact. It should be kept in mind that the propaganda items were stated, pushed and repeatedly set forth by those who had a financial interest in the manufacturing, sale, promotion and advertising of liquor.

PROPAGANDA

"People drank more during prohibition. When you tell an American he can't drink he will drink to show his independence."

Prohibition was NOT a failure in the amount of liquor consumed.

The "great wave of Prohibition" began in 1915. The succeeding years saw wartime Prohibition (1918) and constitutional Prohibition (1920).

The government recorded consumption of all alcoholic beverages in 1914, the last year of "normal" drinking, was 22.80 gallons per capita. In 1920, it was 2.48 gallons per capita (plus illicit or "bootleg liquor"). However, the total consumption was estimated by *"The New Crusade,"* a handbook of the "wets," as no more than 8.96 gallons per capita. This is about a 60% decrease when compared to the 1914 consumption.

In 1934, the first full year of Repeal, the government once again reported the total per capita consumption as only 8.36. This was when the drinkers could purchase and consume as much as they wanted.

Did consumption decline during the Prohibition era even if law enforcement erroded in some metropolitan areas?

The chart shown on page 119 shows how the consumption of beer dropped during the Prohibition era. Even after legalization in 1933 the per capita ratio was one-half of the pre-Prohibition Era.

Per Capita Consumption of Beer 1900-1975 (in Gallons)

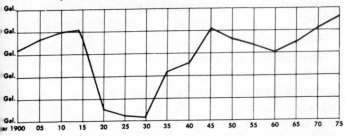

The "Historical Statistics of the United States" (U.S. Dept. of Commerce and Bureau of Census) gives the following population and amount of beer produced for each year since 1900. Shown are the figures for each fifth year.

Year	Population of U.S.	Gallons of Beer	Gallons per Capita
1900	76,094,000	1,224,500,000	16.09
1905	84,090,000	1,534,500,000	18.24
1910	92,407,000	1,844,500,000	19.96
1914	98,918,000	2,052,200,000	20.74
1915	100,546,000	1,853,800,000	18.43
1920	106,461,000	285,200,000*	2.67
1925	115,829,000	158,100,000*	1.36
1930	123,077,000	114,111,000*	0.92
1934	126,415,000	1,168,018,000	9.23
1935	127,250,000	1,402,099,000	11.01
1940	131,954,000	1,701,652,000	12.89
1945	132,481,000	2,684,724,000	20.26
1950	151,235,000	2,753,017,000	18.20
1955	164,308,000	2,783,521,000	16.94
1960	179,979,000	2,930,988,000	16.28
1965	193,526,000	3,348,465,000	17.30
1970	203,810,000	4,174,274,000	20.48
1975	213,100,000	4,893,970,000	22.96

*See note on next page.

*During the Prohibition era (1920-1933) the breweries produced "near beer" which contained less than ½ of 1% alcohol. Also many converted to producing industrial alcohol.

Note that the per capita consumption of beer after Prohibition was *less* than one-half the per capita consumption of the pre-Phohibition era.

The *production* of beer did not reach the 1914 level until the year of 1943, but the *per capita consumption level was lower*.

Population 1943	Gal. of Beer 1943	Gal. Per Capita
133,971,000	2,201,558,000	16.43

What does the above suggest? It points out most vividly that the Prohibition Era had "weaned" a good percentage of the population away from the use of alcoholic beverages. Can this be considered a failure? The only ones who really believe Prohibition was a failure are (1) those who profit from the sale of America's most abused drug and (2) those who believe the propaganda of the alcohol-drug pushers.

The above chart and figures deals exclusively with beer. Below are shown the per capita consumption of liquor as published by the Distilled Spirits Industry (1975 Annual Statistical Review). These figures do not include wines.

Year	Gallons Per Capita	Year	Gallons Per Capita
1934	.046	1945	1.44
1935	0.70	1950	1.26
1936	0.95	1955	1.21
1937	1.05	1960	1.31
1938	0.98	1965	1.52
1939	1.03	1970	1.82
1940	1.10	1975	1.97

The figures in the box on page 120 show how little was actually consumed after the end of Prohibition in 1933. In 1934 the consumption of liquor was less than $\frac{1}{2}$ gallon per capita. By 1975, the per capita was almost 2 gallons or over 300% increase.

In spite of the tremendous increase in the per capita consumption of liquor the industry is never satisfied. *"Fortune"* magazine (September 1977) tells of new, aggressive marketing strategies being planned by the distillers to increase sales.

The new agressive "pitch" will be made to various group as to women, ethnic groups, and especially to "the more than 84 million adults whom sociologists define as light or moderate drinkers — people who consume as little as a few drinks a month. If half of them could be persuaded to take even one additional drink of whiskey a month, the industry would sell almost 2.5 million cases a year more."

However, the main "pitch" of the distillers will be to the gullibility of the public. This calls for ad copy that can sell, such as stressing that their brand adds "'character' which in their terms has less to do with taste than with what a drinker thinks about his drink." This "character" projection is seed, for example, in the pushing of Chivas Regal, one of the highest priced brands, although it probably came from the same vat as a brand selling for half the price. The purchaser is made to feel he has gained an elevation in status by the purchase of the higher priced "elite" or "more prestigious" brand.

The selling of whiskey has specialized in sales promotion and advertising. The average purchaser of liquor does not know that there are over 20,000 registered brands of liquor and that the vast majority of the contents of these brands came from only a few vats. The *Fortune* article points out that American Distillers, one of the smaller distilleries which ranks fourteenth in the industry has recently "lopped off no fewer than 250 marginal or money-losing brands, leaving it with a present total of around fifty."

In the selling of whiskey the customer is most certainly on the "sucker list" of the distiller. The liquor industry has a vested interest in more and heavier drinking.

PROPAGANDA
"Prohibition was a failure!"

Prohibition was NOT a failure when alcoholism, poverty, crime, etc. are considered.

Prof. Henry W. Farnam of Yale University wrote about the first two years of Prohibition,

"We see that Prohibition has produced just the kind of effect that was desired. It would be difficult to find in all the history of social legislation a case where the effect of a law can be traced so quickly and so accurately. For we find uniformly, in spite of many conflicting forces which affect all laws, that . . . Prohibition, when carried out in good faith . . . is capable of diminishing with a speed which would have seemed impossible twenty years ago, death from alcoholism, drunkenness, poverty due to liquor, and much crime." ("*The Law of the Land and Our Moral Frontier*")

President Charles W. Eliot of Harvard University had been an opponent of Prohibition, but he wrote the Massachusetts legislature stating:

"Evidence has accumulated on every hand that Prohibition has promoted public health, public happiness and industrial efficiency. This evidence comes from manufacturers, physicians, nurses of all sorts (school, factory, hospital and district) and from social workers of many races and religions laboring daily in a great variety of fields. This testimony also demonstrates beyond a doubt that Prohibition is actually sapping the terrible forces of disease, poverty, crime and vice." (From a letter sent Feb. 17, 1922 to Hearings of the Massachusetts Legislature).

Prohibition was NOT a failure economically.

Professor Paul Douglas, research specialist in changes in American wage levels, called attention to the unprecedented increase in hourly real wages and concluded by stating:

"It may not be without significance that the increase in real wages on any appreciable scale first began in 1917 when the Prohibition laws of the various states and the war-time restrictions of the national government greatly reduced the amount of liquor sold. The real rise of real wages was particularly marked during the years of 1919-1923 when the enforcement of the prohibitory amendment was probably more effective than immediately thereafter." (*"An Economist Looks at Prohibition"* H. F. Miller, 1930)

Thomas A. Edison, the inventor, noting what had developed in his State of New Jersey, before Senate Hearings in 1930, said,

"I feel that Prohibition is the greatest experiment yet made to benefit man." (National Prohibition Amendment Hearings, February 1930, page 658)

Honorable George S. Hobart (Governor of New Jersey) reported that in New Jersey,

"At the end of 1922 there were thirty more savings banks and trust companies than at the end of 1917; 431 more building and loan associations; 357,522 more building and loan association members; 40,917 more depositors in savings banks; and an increase in five years of 92.5% in deposits, viz. $655,569,944." (*Annals of the American Academy of Political and Social Science,* Sept. 1923)

Between 1920 and 1929, new life insurance written increased from $6,960,168,000 to $12,751,428,000.

Assets of Savings and loans associations increased under Prohibition from $2,033,000,000 in 1920 to $7,082,000,000 in 1929. Bank deposits increased from $15,834,000,000 in 1920 to $28,992,000,000 in 1924.

Arthur Brisbane, editor of the Hearst newspapers, was not a "dry" and did not want Prohibition, nevertheless he wrote of Prohibition:

"One hundred percent efficiency has been added at one stroke of the people of America, half of the misery of half of the people has been abolished. Three hundred thousand traps have been closed into which a considerable portion of the youth of the country fell every year. The suppression of the drunk traffic is an expression of the highest morality upon which we are entering." (*"Brisbane"* A. Carlson, p. 250)

Prohibition was NOT a failure in public and mental health.

Dr. Haven Emerson of Columbia University stated:

"Whenever the records are obtained for first admissions for alcoholic psychosis or for all admissions for alcoholic psychosis to mental hospitals, the evidence is very definite that in 1919, 1920, and in 1921, a lower level was reached than had ever occurred before (*Survey Graphic,* Dec.

1928, p. 330). He further points out how the rate of deaths from nephritis, Bright's disease and pneumonia was the lowest ever. For tuberculosis the death rate from 1911 to 1917 was constant,— "Then it fell in the seven years of Prohibition (1920-1926) at a faster rate than at any previous period in our history. This was the first practical evidence we have ever had of the astounding effect on the mortality of the country of making alcohol relatively inaccessible." (Senate Judiciary Committee Hearings, April 1926 pp. 787, 789, 792).

The U. S. National Center for Health Statistics have traced the deaths in the U. S. due to cirrhosis of the liver. The following chart based on the National Center for Health Statistics bears out the fact that National Prohibition (1917 to 1933) brought about a tremendous decline in deaths due to cirrhosis. When Prohibition ended the increase in deaths corresponds closely to the increase in consumption.

Mortality Rate Deaths (Per 100,000) From Cirrhosis in the United States

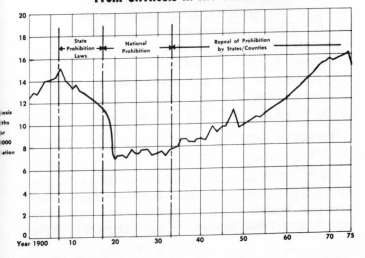

The chart below gives the per capita consumption of the population aged 15 years and over. Note how the consumption of alcohol parallels the deaths from cirrhosis (page 125). With the decrease in consumption comes the decrease in cirrhotic deaths.

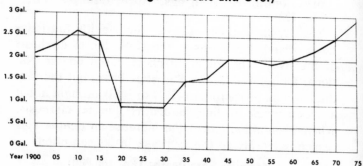

Per Capita Consumption of Absolute Alcohol
(Population Age 15 Years and Over)

If Prohibition failed—it failed to create alcoholics who died with cirrhosis. Ninety-nine percent of cirrhotic deaths are caused from alcohol. Prohibition, even though poorly enforced, brought significant public health gains to society as a whole.

Alcoholism declined so markedly during that era that the alcoholic hospitals went out of business and the alcoholic wards of city hospitals were emptied.

Prohibition was NOT a failure to the working classes.

A prominent business magazine of the 1920's *The Manufacturers Record* sent a questionnaire to hundreds of leading men of business, industry, commerce and labor leaders whose statements were published under the title: "The Prohibition Question." Here are a few:

"I am not a Prohibitionist myself, but look upon this matter purely from a scientific and common-sense standpoint. In my own business, conditions have been greatly improved since our employees no longer have free and unlimited use of liquor; and from conversations I have had with hundreds of retail merchants throughout the country, I am convinced that the theory that the country in general would be benefited by Prohibition has been a proven fact." —Edward Freschi, President, Holeproof Hosiery Co., Milwaukee, Wis.

"In Detroit, the favorable effects of Prohibition are apparent even to a blind man, and this is despite the fact that we are but across the river from wet Canada and have a large population accustomed to drinking liquor." —Henry M. Leland, President, Lincoln Motor Company.

"Am glad to advise you Prohibition has done wonders in our city." —H. B. Smith, Secretary and Treasurer, McInnes Steel Co., Ltd., Carry, Pennsylvania.

"Less lost time, less accidents, less incompetence, less carelessness and inefficiency, better work, better houses, more thrift, happier families, and sober and safer and more efficient men, who now are finding out what it means really to live where they formerly merely existed." —George M. Verity, President, American Rolling Mill Co., Middletown, Ohio.

"I find a marked improvement in the number of men who are saving their money and who own their houses or are buying their houses, and I find a decided improvement in the home life of the workers due to the fact that the women and children have more food, more clothing and better care in every way. Back of all that, the worker takes his family and goes to the picture show or to the park now, where he formerly spent his evenings in the saloon drinking and spending his money." —W. S. Stone, Ground Chief, Brotherhood of Locomotive Engineers, Cleveland, Ohio.

Andre Siegfried, opponent of Prohibition, had to acknowledge that "One can go through whole regions without seeing any liquor or meeting a single drunkard. The great mass of the people are undoubtedly benefiting in health, standard of living, working efficiency, and in increased wages." (*"America Comes of Age"*, Andre Siegfried, p. 89)

If space permitted similar quotations from hundreds of business executives, labor union leaders, researchers, educators and analysts could be given here, each testifying to the FACT that the economic, public health, social problems have all been aided by restricting the manufacturing and selling of alcoholic beverages.

PROPAGANDA
"The Eighteenth Amendment was an unenforceable law."

When all the facts are laid out it is surprising that the 18th Amendment worked as well as it did.

The main reason for poor law enforcement under Prohibition was best explained by Senator Burton K. Wheeler of Montana when he stated at the hearings before House Committee on Civil Service (1926)

"The reason Prohibition has not been successful is that they have appointed as head of the Treasury and Prohibition Enforcement a man who has been in the whiskey business for the last forty years. I refer to Andrew W. Mellon."

There were many reasons why Andrew W. Mellon

should never have been granted the task of enforcing dry legislation. The *Saturday Blade* of Chicago, November 5, 1921 carried an article by Mr. Boyce who stated, "when President Harding selected A. W. Mellon, the Pittsburgh banker, brewer, distiller, street-railway and trust magnet as Secretary of the United States Treasury, the whole country was shocked and believed then, as it does now, that it was not a personal selection of the President, but was forced upon him by the politicians . . . The amount of his contribution to the Republican campaign fund has never been disclosed and no doubt never will be, because it would be put through different names and paid into the campaign fund by others than himself."

The enforcement of the Prohibition laws should have been in the hands of the Department of Justice and not the Secretary of the Treasury. But the power of party politics and wheeling and dealing congressmen took this vital action to see the Eighteenth Amendment nullified. Congressman Story of Texas is quoted in the Congressional Record (March 16, 1933 p. 527) saying "I feel I am stating the truth when I say the administration of the Volstead Act by the Secretary of the Treasury is largely responsible for all the outlawry to the nation for the past twelve years. . . . He (Mellon) was opposed to the 18th Amendment and practically said to the bootlegger . . . The United States is open to you." (abridged).

The complete disrespect for law and order, for honesty and integrity in officials reached its lowest ebb in the Harding-Mellon era, and the depths of its corruption makes the exploits of the Nixon-Watergate escapade seem like kids play. For a detailed and documented review of the Mellon Era see *"The Wrecking of the 18th Amendment"* by Ernest Gordon.

PROPAGANDA
"Prohibition caused crime and gang warfare!"

Gangs existed long before Prohibition.

At the turn of the century it was the Dutch Zellers mob that controlled the Ohio River cities. Other gangs existed all across the U.S. They didn't derive most of their revenues from liquor during the Prohibition era, but rather, their big money came from gambling and prostitution. They existed before Prohibition, continued during Prohibition and have become even larger and nationally syndicated since the legalization of liquor in 1933.

A man who had thoroughly studied the crime scene is Mr. John Landesco. Research Director of the American Institute of Criminal Law and Criminology. He wrote in the *Annals of the American Academy of Political and Social Science* (Sept. 1932) the following:

"Gangs and syndicates did not originate with Prohibition. . . . The names which loomed large in the chieftainship of the bootlegging industry were traceable to gambling and vice-syndicates which existed under dynasties of rulers or bosses for years prior to Prohibition . . . the same political partiality and same likelihood to expose violators in the enemy faction occurred under regulatory laws."

The basic fact remains that the promoters of liquor today as well as during the Prohibition era have done and are still doing more to promote disrespect for law and order than any other one group in the history of our nation.

Today we find the promoters of liquor laugh at any regulatory restrictions that are placed upon the selling of liquor. They encourage their friends to break the law if a state, county, city or precinct has a restriction against the sale of liquor by the drink, or Sunday and holiday closing, or sale to those under age, or drinking and driving.

These liquor promoters become very indignant when one charges them with being law breakers, drug pushers, or un-American. But who in our great nation has done more to encourage their sons and daughters to adopt a philosophy of life which says if you don't like the law break it? By example the parent who demands liquor be served at a restaurant in a restricted or prohibited area has directly or indirectly told his children that his demands are more important than the law. Result: disrespect for law and order.

PROPAGANDA

"Prohibition was forced upon the nation when over one million American soldiers were overseas during World War I."

If every soldier overseas had voted against Prohibition (which is doubtful) and his vote returned to his own congressional district, it would have made no difference in the outcome of the elections because the vote was overwhelming for congressmen and legislators who were "dry".

The Eighteenth Amendment was submitted to the state legislatures by vote of the U. S. Congress. The vote in the U. S. House of Representatives was 281 to 128, and in the U. S. Senate it was 65 to 20. The Amendment was then ratified by 46 of the 48 state legislatures in only 13 months. The aggregate votes in the various state Senates of the ratifying states was 84% in favor of the Eighteenth Amendment. The votes in the state Houses of Representatives in favor of the Amendment was 79%. Rhode Island and Connecticut were the two states failing to ratify the Eighteenth Amendment. No other amendment to the U. S. Consitution has ever received as high a percentage of ratification as did the Prohibition Amendment!

This argument as all "wet" propaganda did not tell the truth. The drive for Prohibition began in 1851 when the state of Maine adopted Prohibition. Kansas did the same in 1880. By April 1, 1917 Prohibition had been adopted by 26 states. This was before "the boys went overseas." Seven additional states adopted prohibition after that date.

Prohibition swept through the states because the people were concerned that government should not license that which is detrimental to the general welfare. A long series of court cases stated that "There is no inherent right in a citizen to sell intoxicating liquors." (U. S. Supreme Ct., Crowley vs. Christensen, 137 U. S. 86 11 Sup. Ct. 13). By 1917 the 26 states that had adopted a prohibition law were as follows:

State	Prohibition Adopted	State	Prohibition Adopted
Maine	1851	Oklahoma	1907
Kansas	1880	Mississippi	1908
North Dakota	1889	North Carolina	1908
Georgia	1907	Tennessee	1909

State	Prohibition Adopted	State	Prohibition Adopted
West Virginia	1912	Idaho	1915
Virginia	1914	South Carolina	1915
Oregon	1914	Montana	1916
Washington	1914	South Dakota	1916
Colorado	1914	Michigan	1916
Arizona	1914	Nebraska	1916
Alabama	1915	Indiana	1917
Arkansas	1915	Utah	1917
Iowa	1915	New Hampshire	1917

Seven states adopted prohibition laws after April 1, 1917. All prior to national prohibition or the enactment of the Eighteenth Amendment.

State	Year	State	Year
New Mexico	1917	Florida	1918
Texas	1918	Nevada	1918
Ohio	1918	Kentucky	1919
Wyoming	1918		

Prohibition had been adopted by state legislatures and the U. S. Congress that had been elected on the Prohibition issue.

Felex Frankfurter, Justice of the Supreme Court of the United States, who had not been in favor of prohibition, wrote in the *Annals of the Academy of Political and Social Science*, (Sept. 1923, p. 193.)

"It is sheer caricature to convey the impression that the Eighteenth Amendment came like a thief in the night. Prohibition was the culmination of fifty years of continuous effort; nor did the movement lack alert, persistent, and powerful opposition. If the process by which this amendment came into the Constitution is open to question, one hardly dare contemplate the moral justification of some of the other amendments to the Constitution itself."

PROPAGANDA

"The movement to end Prohibition was the rising of the masses against the law."

The "masses" brought Prohibition to the nation but a small group of multimillionaires were the initial organizers of a concerted effort to destroy the law of the land which had been approved by the voters.

The hearings of a sub-committee of the Committee on the Judiciary (U.S. Senate, 71st Congress, Second Session) brought out the facts about a handful of people, all millionaires, who met in April of 1919 and incorporated an organization known as the Association Against the Prohibition Amendment. The AAPA, as this group was known, had one specific goal—to make the 18th Amendment forever inoperative. During the Senate investigation it was brought out that only 53 men had been responsible for contributing 75% of the entire fund of the Association during one year.

The investigation revealed that this group of industrial, financial and social leaders of America who claimed they were seeking to promote the general welfare, to put an end to bootlegging, drunkenness, hypocrisy and political corruption were in reality seeking a way to get rid of their income taxes!

The personal contributions of this group of millionaires was only a small part of the support they threw behind the Association Against the Prohibition Amendment. Through their interlocking directorates they controlled over forty-billion dollars of invested funds. With this power structure at their command they could determine the policy of a great many powerful newspapers and magazines. By determining the editorial policy of newspapers and magazines the AAPA could brainwash the readers of such publications. And this they did.

The tactics employed by AAPA controlled publications varied, but the end result was the same. For example, if a bootlegger was arrested or shot at by a law enforcement officer the newspaper account usually made the Prohibition agent look like a criminal and the bootlegger was the mistreated victim of an evil law enforcement agent.

Fletcher Dobyns, in his book *"The Amazing Story of Repeal"* deals with the power of propaganda. He points up the basic truth that

"every interest that has something to put over through the manipulation of public opinion, has on hand its corps of professional propagandists. Whether known as ministers of propaganda, public relations counsels, publicity men, or by any other name, the business of these men is to poison the wells of information. They take advantage of ignorance, engage in suppression and fabrication, excite fear and hatred, ponder to prejudice and ridicule and defame honest men who endeavor to oppose them."

No group of men and women have done more to poison the wells of information than have the liquor interests, and especially was this true of the Association Against the Prohibition Amendment.

The Honorable Louis C. Cramton, addressing the national House of Representatives on January 21, 1924 said the AAPA "is an organization opposed to law enforcement, promoting, thriving upon and rejoicing at triumph of crime and disorder over law and order."

The AAPA's purpose was to prevent the enforcement of a law that had been passed by Congress and to render inoperative a provision of the Constitution of the United States. However, the AAPA concealed their real motives. If they had announced their real purpose, which was to save the profits of the liquor industry, they would have been greeted with contempt by the public in general. Rather, they pretended that their purpose was to save the Constitution of the United States by "keeping the powers of the several states separated from those of the federal government."

One of the most publicized cases of propaganda news reporting revolved around what was called the "St. Valentine's Day Massacre."

The "St. Valentine's Day Massacre" took place on February 14, 1929 in Chicago, Illinois. Actually the entire incident shows how well Prohibition was working in its goal of cutting alcohol consumption.

The flow of booze in Chicago in 1929 was limited. There was bootleg liquor but it was not "flowing" as the wet newspapers claim. Just prior to Valentine's Day in 1929, a Chicago gangster by the name of "Bugs" Moran sent six of his most trusted "hoods" all the way to Detroit to pick up 150 cases of Canadian liquor that had been smuggled across the Detroit River and were stored at Grosse Isle just south of Detroit. The 150 cases of booze were placed in three panel trucks with 50 cases per truck. There were two of Moran's men in each truck.

When the three trucks arrived in Chicago on Valentine's Day they were driven into a garage on north LaSalle Street. No sooner had the trucks driven into the garage when a "police car" loaded with police officers with machine guns pulled into the garage. There was the rat-a-tat-tat of the guns and the "police" drove the three booze laden trucks out of the garage.

In the garage lay six dead gangsters all of whom were wanted on murder charges. The police officers were not actually policemen but were Al Capone's gangsters disguised as police officers. The AAPA controlled newspaper headlines cried out "Mass Murder," and in editorial comment laid the blame on prohibition.

What does the "St. Valentine's Day Massacre", as the wet newspapers termed this gang war, really tell us? (1.) It shows that a gang war can start over 150 cases of liquor, which in turn points out that bootleg liquor was not as plentiful as the wet propagandists would have the people believe. (2.) It shows how the wet controlled newspapers can get public concern stirred up because six murderers were killed. Yet those same newspapers are seemingly unconcerned that every day in 1977 there were 76 persons slaughtered on the highways of the United States by drinking drivers.

The basic control of the Association against the Prohibition Amendment lay in the hands of five multimillionaires: The three DuPont brothers, (Pierre, Irenne, and Lammot), John J. Raskob, vice-president of the DuPont Company and Charles H. Sabin, chairman of the board of the Guaranty Company of New York as well as director of sixteen large corporations. These five men were the "power" behind the AAPA, and using their corporate leverage sent letters asking heads of corporations for contributions to the yearly million dollar basic budget to destroy the constitutional will of the people.

At the time of the Senate investigation the president of AAPA, Mr. Henry H. Curran, reported that 75 per cent of the budget was received from 53 million-aires. Senator Robinson of Indiana, in questioning Mr. Curran, stated, "I am only mentioning that 53 men are furnishing you the sinews of war for your campaign, and 53 men does not constitute a vast majority."

The movement to end Prohibition was not the rising of the masses against the law but rather it was a carefully laid plan by which the American public was brainwashed by a small group of million-aires seeking financial benefits for themselves. The control of the press by either ownership, or purchase of the editorial policy of the newspapers and maga-zines and by advertising and being able to command the free use of millions of dollars worth of space in these publications they were able "to poison the wells of information."

The association disbursed further propaganda against the Eighteenth Amendment by writing speeches for prominent congressmen to deliver thereby getting free news coverage for their cause.

An interesting sidelight on this era is the fact that Pierre DuPont was a dry during the first five years of the AAPA. In fact the DuPonts absolutely pro-hibited the use of any alcoholic beverages by their employees in their many plants. However, they changed their position in 1926 when Pierre DuPont decided that legalizing liquor would reduce the cor-porate taxes on his companies by taxing the sale of liquor. Though the DuPonts were thoroughly aware of the evils of the liquor traffic and the social and economic benefits of Prohibition they never permitted public welfare, love of country, or common honesty to interfere with their pursuit of profits.

In a circular sent out to the large income taxpayers of the country, Pierre DuPont said:

"As our average tax collection for the years 1923-26 from individuals and corporations were $1,817,000,000, resulting in a considerable surplus, it is fair to say that the British liquor policy applied in the United States would permit the total abolition of the income tax both personal and corporate."

PROPAGANDA
"Prohibition does not prohibit."

"That 'prohibition does not prohibit' is the most common and also the most effective argument of saloon keepers. The mere statement of the proposition is an impeachment of the saloon, not of the prohibitory statute. If prohibition will not prohibit, it is because, in the first place, saloon keepers are not law abiding citizens, but are naturally law defiers and law violators. It means that saloon keepers do not respect the law, but always resist it. Nullification of the law is the creed of the average saloon keeper.

"The natural and inherent tendency of the business is to engender and foster a spirit of anarchy. As a rule, the average saloon keeper has no more respect for the law and the right of society than the safe-blower, the burglar or highwayman. The object of the safe-blower, the burglar and highwayman is to procure another's property without injuring him personally, but it is the mission of the saloon keeper not only to procure the property of his neighbor, but to injure him mentally, physicaly, morally and socially.

"That this estimate of the average saloon keeper is correct there is no doubt, and it is certainly not unfair to them to quote their own declaraion, as admissions.

"The liquor journal, *The National Advocate*, says: 'In our meetings the saloon men merely demand the right to defy any man who shall impose upon them any law that is against them. Such laws ought to be defied; they should be trampled in the dust; and if they can not be revised, then we say it is time to become anarchists'."   —Samuel R. Artman
Judge of the 20th Judicial
Circuit Court of Indiana

The above quotation was made in 1908 in the book "*The Legalized Outlaw*" by Judge Artman, p. 178.

Has this "legalized outlaw" changed in any degree? Are the saloon keepers of 1978 any more law abiding than the saloon keepers of 1908? Does the present day liquor industry have any more respect for the statute laws on the constitution of any state than did the brewers and distillers of the early 1900's? — or of the Prohibition era of 1920-1933?

Whether it be the saloon keeper, the liquor store retailer, or the manufacturer, the beer-liquor industry has basically made no change in their philosophy. The reason is self evident. They are driven by the profit motive. They know what their product is — an anaesthetic, narcotic, toxic drug — they know their products can and does create the alcoholic; they know it destroys the home, causes a highway traffic slaughter, helps fill our jails, but as servants of Bacchus, the God of wine and drink, and worshipping at the shrine of mammonism, they continue on their evil way.

Pick any year, choose any state and check the court cases. Hundreds of cases each year revolve around the liquor business as they violate laws, circumvent and bend laws, rules, regulations, or restrictions for one purpose — more profit.

The beer and liquor industry is a close knit trust. Although the production is growing by leaps and bounds, the number of breweries and distillers is being rapidly decreased. This unification of interests makes possible the mighty power manifest in the domination of state and federal government, the control of political nominations, and the "investment" in campaign funds of state legislators and U. S. Congressmen, and the control of city administrators.

Prohibition doesn't prohibit? Prohibition shuts off the manufacturing and selling of alcoholic products and thereby hits at the very source of the many alcohol problems that society faces today. The power of money in the hands of the unscrupulous, law defying liquor industry has been basic to the moral decline of our nation.

Prohibition does work! Prohibition *did* change the American drinking habits. In *Tap and Tavern,* December 9, 1968, Robert W. Coyne, President of the Distilled Spirits Institute, Inc. in the article "D.S.I. Marks 35th Anniversary" says, "The early days of Repeal saw limited personal acceptance of alcoholic beverages with only 22 percent of the adults being consumers. Today, 71 percent of the adults are consumers."

The people of the United States accepted prohibition for what it was — an attempt to have a people free of the drug that can and does destroy the individual, the family and society. The living of a full, well rounded, alcohol-free way of living is not in the interest of the greedy liquor traffic, and that is why they fight so hard against *any* restriction in the sale of this drug.

PROPAGANDA

"Prohibition won't work until public opinion is educated to accept it."

This baseless argument was disproven by one of the states that did not vote to ratify the 18th Amendment. All of the five congressional representatives from Connecticut voted against the Eighteenth Amendment. The majority of the population of Connecticut were of recent foreign extraction and the state press was definitely prejudiced against prohibition.

Nevertheless, as Professor Henry W. Farnam of Yale pointed out, the blessings of prohibition descended upon Connecticut, in his book *"The Law of the Land and Our Moral Frontier."*

1. Prisoners in Connecticut jails charged with drunkenness fell from 7,314 in 1917 to 943 in 1920.
2. Arrests for assault and breach of peace declined to less than one-third.
3. Jail commitments for vagrancy practically vanished.
4. Commitments for alcohol insanity in 1920 were less than one-third the number of 1917.
5. Death rate from alcoholism and cirrhosis in 1920 was less than one-half the 1917 rate.

6. Accidental deaths in 1917 were 10.7 to 10,000, in 1920 it was 7.3.

7. Automobile death rate fell by 40%.

8. Death rate from tuberculosis dropped from 15.3 per 10,000 to 9.6 in 1921.

9. Death from pneumonia, to which alcoholics are particularly liable, fell by over 50%.

Not only did Connecticut benefit from prohibition in spite of the people's opposition to it, but every state found similar relief from the problems caused by alcohol.

The dictionary says:

BAMBOOZLE is to trick; hornswaggle; also, to perplex and baffle.

The liquor industry, its product and its propaganda qualify as "the bamboozler of the century."